SALT AFFECTED SOILS AND THEIR MANAGEMENT

About the Author

Dr. D. Prasad (b. 1948) retired Professor and Head, I.A.R.I., New Delhi, has more than 40 years of research and teaching experience in the field of nematology in particular and plant protection in general. Dr. Prasad is known for his research contributions in nematode management on groundnut and soybean and developed IPM nodule for root knot nematode on groundnut. He also worked on environmentally safe pesticides, developed and tested two new molecules for control of nematodes and hence sent to ICAR for Patening, and received HARDF Award for 1994. Dr. Prasad has written/edited various books. He founded a Society of Plant Protection Sciences in 1992 which publishes biannual Journal "Annals of Plant Protection Sciences".

Dr. Ravi Prakash Maurya, did his M.Sc. (Ag.) from D.D.U., Gorakhpur University and Ph.D. (Agril. Extension) from C.S.J.M. University, Kanpur. He worked in K.V.K. at various places in Bihar and U.P. Published 125 articles in Hindi and English for farmers, 26 research papers, 25 abstracts in national/ international conferences and 2 books, guided 3 students. Recently working as Project Co-ordinator-cum-Professor, K.V.K. (NDUA & T, Faizabad) Ambedkar Nagar, U.P. He has chaired different meetings/symposia/conferences and conducted Kisan Mela, Kisan Gosthi etc. and other extension activities at district and state level.

Salt Affected Soils and their Management

D. PRASAD
RAVI PRAKASH MAURYA

Ekta Book Distributors
Delhi • Guwahati • Visakhapatnam

EKTA BOOK DISTRIBUTORS
4649-B/21, Ansari Road
Daryaganj, New Delhi - 110 002
Phones: 23263193, 9435116718
Email: ektabooks@yahoo.com
Visit us: www.akanshapublishinghouse.com

Salt Affected Soils and their Management

First Published, 2014

ISBN 978-81-923230-5-3

PRINTED IN INDIA

Published by Akansha Publishing House, New Delhi - 110 002 and Printed at Harmain Offset Press, Delhi.

Contents

Preface

Soil is a complex body can accommodate all types of abiotic and biotic factors which are responsible for their quality and productivity. A number of abiotic factors through an array of soil inhabit micro-organisms that may be responsible for interference with crop productivity. Under intensive farming system there is a growing tendency to apply higher doses of fertilizers and pesticides. These external chemical inputs over a period of time influence soil health and the capacity to sustain higher crop products on and productivity. The abiotic factors such as formation soil from parental rock, temperature, regime, hydrology and ultimately salt formation. Such conditions deteriorate the soil productivity and health. Hydrology or efficient water management however enhance the crop production and soil health but inadequate drainage result in water logging and salinity problems. Such problems are very much in the coastal regions wherein water rich in salt submerge the agricultural field and upon drying the salt deposit on the soil surface. This lead to formation of salty soil where no or selected crops may be grown.

Salt affected soils are relatively more extensive in arid and semi arid regions. Therefore, their management in a prophylactic manner is a need of the hour. The book entitled

"Salt Affected Soils and their Management" bring out the causes and remedies to tackle the nationwide problem in an effective manner to grow crops suitable to the area for sustainable and eco-friendly manner.

Authors

1

Introduction

Accumulation of excess salts in the root zone resulting in a partial or complete loss of soil productivity is a worldwide phenomenon. The problems of soil salinity are most widespread in the arid and semi-arid regions but salt affected soils also occur extensively in sub-humid and humid climates, particularly in the coastal regions where the ingress of sea water through estuaries and rivers and through groundwater causes large-scale salinization. Soil salinity is also a serious problem in areas where groundwater of high salt content is used for irrigation. The most serious salinity problems are being faced in the irrigated arid and semi-arid regions of the world and it is in these very regions that irrigation is essential to increase agricultural production to satisfy food requirements. However, irrigation is often costly, technically complex and requires skilled management. Failure to apply efficient principles of water management may result in wastage of water through seepage; over-watering and inadequate drainage result in waterlogging and salinity problems which reduce the soil productivity, eventually leading to loss of cultivable land.

Researcher calculated from various available data that the world as a whole is losing at least ten hectare of arable land every minute, five because of soil erosion, three from soil salinization, one from other soil degradation processes and one from non-agricultural uses. The problem of soil degradation is a serious threat to the welfare of mankind. Although degradation of the land has always characterized man's systematic use of it, the process has accelerated in recent decades and precisely at a time when population growth and rising expectations have begun to demand enormous increases in food production. The problem is of overwhelming urgency. As the soil is subject to degradation, the cost of reclaiming it becomes higher, rising sharply until the threshold is passed beyond which reclamation is no longer economically feasible. Nearly 50 per cent of the irrigated land in the arid and semi-arid regions have some degree of soil salinization problems. This figure indicates the magnitude of the problem that must be tackled in order to meet future global food needs.

It is generally agreed that the future food needs of increasing population will be met by directing the efforts of all concerned towards:

- improving the level of management of soils already under cultivation, and
- by bringing under plough the potentially arable soils which are presently uncultivated.

Soil salinity is a major impediment in achieving increased crop yields by either of the above approaches. It is in realization of this that the United Nations Conference on Desertification held in Nairobi in 1977 adopted the following recommendations:

"It is recommended that urgent measures be taken to combat desertification in the irrigated lands by preventing and controlling waterlogging, salinization and sodication by modifying farming techniques to increase productivity in a regular and sustained way; by developing new irrigation and drainage schemes where appropriate always using an integrated approach; and through improvement of the social and economic conditions of people dependent on irrigated agriculture."

The problems of salt-affected soils are old but their magnitude and their intensity have been increasing fast due to large-scale efforts to bring additional areas under irrigation in recent decades. The problems have been made worse by development of irrigation systems without adequate provision for drainage and are being aggravated by poor water management practices and unsound reclamation procedures.

The general characteristics and basic principles involved in the identification, reclamation and management of salt-affected soils are the same throughout the world. However, differences from place to place in soil characteristics, climate, water availability, farm management capability, financial resources, available inputs and economic incentives lead to differences in method, extent and rapidity of soil reclamation. Although technical literature abounds with sound information on the subject, nonetheless, there are far too many partial or complete failures of efforts to reclaim salt-affected soils. These failures, due largely to lack of proper identification and subsequent use of incorrect reclamation methods, result in losses of both money and potential increases in crop production. This publication presents a brief summary of information which will be particularly useful in the proper identification, reclamation and management of soils with problems caused by the presence of excess salts.

ORIGIN, CLASSIFICATION AND DISTRIBUTION OF SALT-AFFECTED SOILS

Salt-affected soils occur in all continents and under almost all climatic conditions. Their distribution, however, is relatively more extensive in the arid and semi-arid regions compared to the humid regions. The nature and properties of these soils are also diverse such that they require specific approaches for their reclamation and management to maintain their long term productivity. For any long-term solutions, it is, therefore, necessary to understand the mode of origin of salt-affected soils and to classify them, keeping in view the physico-chemical characteristics, processes leading to their formation and the likely approaches for their reclamation and successful management.

Origin of Salts

The presence of excess salts on the soil surface and in the root zone characterizes all saline soils. The main source of all salts in the soil is the primary minerals in the exposed layer of the earth's crust. During the process of chemical weathering which involves hydrolysis, hydration, solution, oxidation, carbonation and other processes, the salt constituents are gradually released and made soluble. The released salts are transported away from their source of origin through surface or groundwater streams. The salts in the groundwater stream are gradually concentrated as the water with dissolved salts moves from the more humid to the less humid and relatively arid areas. The predominant ions near the site of weathering in the presence of carbon dioxide will be carbonates and hydrogen-carbonates of calcium, magnesium, potassium and sodium; their concentrations, however, are low. As the water with dissolved solutes moves from the more humid to the arid regions, the salts are concentrated and the concentration may become high enough to result in precipitation of salts of low solubility. Apart from the precipitation, the chemical constituents of water may undergo further changes through processes of exchange, adsorption, differential mobility, etc., and the net result of these processes invariably is to increase the concentration in respect of chloride and sodium ions in the underground water and in the soils. Researchers recognize the following sequence of changes in the composition of groundwater in relation to their concentrations (Table 1.1) as the water moves from humid to arid areas. Similar trends are observed with regard to the chemical composition of groundwater in India.

Table 1.1: Relationship between the Quantity of Salts in Natural Waters in Relation to their Composition

Nature of water	Total salt concentration, g/l
Siliceous waters - completely fresh waters containing silica and organic substances	0.01 to 0.1
Fresh calcium-bicarbonate waters	0.2 to 0.3
Sodium bicarbonate waters	0.5 to 0.7
Sodium-bicarbonate and carbonate waters containing sulphate and less often chlorides	0.5 to 3.0
Chloride-sulphate waters	2.5 to 5.0
Chloride waters	>5

Geologic materials are highly variable in their elemental composition and some materials are higher in salts than others. Shales, especially those of marine origin, can supply large quantities of soluble salts when traversed by water. Thus the kinds of geologic formations through which the drainage water passes significantly influence the composition and total concentration of salts.

Salts released through weathering in the arid regions with limited rainfall are usually deposited at some depth in the soil profile, the depth depending on such factors as the water retention capacity of the soil, seasonal, annual and maximum rainfall, etc. If the salts are deposited beyond the rooting zone of most crops, say below 150 cm, they rarely affect the crops adversely unless they are redistributed and accumulate in the surface soil layers (Table 1.2).

Table 1.2: Characteristics of an Unirrigated Soil Profile from a Semi-arid Tract

Depth cm	Clay %	pH_s*	ECe (dS/m)
0 - 10	17.3	8.0	1.4
10 - 20	18.5	7.9	0.8
20 - 43	19.0	7.9	0.8
43 - 88	32.5	8.1	1.5
152 - 208	40.8	7.7	4.8
208 - 228	35.8	7.7	11.0

* pH_s - pH measured on soil saturated paste.

Salt-affected soils generally occur in regions that receive salts from other areas and water is the primary carrier. Although the weathering of rocks and minerals is the source of all salts, rarely are the salt-affected soils formed from the accumulation of salts in situ.

Classification

In the course of accumulation of knowledge on the nature, characteristics and plant growth relationships in salt affected soils, two main groups of these soils have been distinguished. These are:

i. **Saline soils** - Soils containing sufficient neutral soluble salts to adversely affect the growth of most crop plants. The soluble salts are chiefly sodium chloride and sodium sulphate. But saline soils also contain appreciable quantities of chlorides and sulphates of calcium and magnesium.

ii. **Sodic soils** - Soils containing sodium salts capable of alkaline hydrolysis, mainly Na_2CO_3, these soils have also been termed as 'Alkali' in older literature.

These two main groups of salt-affected soils differ not only in their chemical characteristics but also in their geographical and geochemical distribution, as well as in their physical and biological properties. The two categories also require different approaches for their reclamation and agricultural utilization. In nature the various sodium salts do not occur absolutely separately, but in most cases either the neutral salts or the ones capable of alkaline hydrolysis exercise a dominant role on the soil-forming processes and therefore in determining soil properties.

Although the above two categories account for a very large fraction of salt affected soils the world over, there are transitional or borderline formations which are likely to have properties intermediate between those of the two broad categories. Several local terms in different parts of the world are in vogue to designate such soils. Other categories of salt-affected soils which, though less extensive, are commonly met in different parts of the world are:

Acid-sulphate Soils

These are soils that have somewhere within a 50 cm depth a pH below 3.5 to 4.0 that is directly or indirectly caused by sulphuric acid formed by the oxidation of pyrite (FeS_2) or, rarely of other reduced sulphur compounds. Potential acid sulphate soils occur in tidal swamps. They have high levels of pyrite, low levels of bases and produce strongly acid sulphate soils when pyrite is oxidized to sulphuric acid after drainage. Pyrite formation is favoured in brackish and saline mangrove swamps dissected by tidal creeks where deposition and build up of coastal sediments is slow. Apart from high salinity, the productivity of acid sulphate soils is restricted due to such soil factors as iron and aluminium toxicities, deficiency of phosphorus, etc.

Degraded Sodic Soils

Degraded sodic soils are usually considered to be an advanced stage of soil development resulting from the washing out of salts. The details of the type of soil developed as the leaching proceeds depends on local conditions, particularly soil texture and type of clay present. As a result of the leaching processes there is a tendency for the dispersed clay and organic matter to move down the profile resulting in the formation of a dark, extremely compact layer having a sharply defined upper surface and merging gradually into the subsoil with increasing depth. The darker colour of the compact layer compared with the layer above may be due to its higher clay content since it does not always have a higher content of organic matter. The upper soil layers have a loose porous, laminar structure due to loss of clay and the upper surfaces of this layer may be paler than the lower, possibly because of silica being deposited on them. The clay pan cracks on drying into well defined vertical columns having a rounded top and smooth, shiny, well defined sides. These can be broken into units about 10 cm high and 5 cm across with a flat base. Below this the column breaks into rather smaller units with flat tops and bottoms which on light crushing break into angular fragments.

As the leaching of these desalinized soils proceeds, the upper horizons deepen and often become slightly acidic in reaction and the amorphous silica content increases. As a further stage of development, it has been suggested that the very characteristic clay pan becomes less pronounced, possibly because of washing down of sandy material from the A horizon in the cracks between the structural units.

There are large areas in western Canada, Australia, USA and other countries where soils having profile morphology typical of solonetz/solod soils are found although sodium forms only a minor proportion of the exchangeable ions. It is possible that these soils originally had enough exchangeable sodium for the solonetz-solod morphology to develop in the profile but that most of this sodium has now been lost through leaching.

A large number of sub-categories of salt-affected soils are recognized in different parts of the world depending on the dominance of a particular chemical constituent (e.g. calcium chloride rich soils or soils containing excessive quantities of exchangeable magnesium - magnesium solonetz, etc.) or a particular morphological character of the soil profile, e.g. presence of a structural 'B' horizon, etc.

Mode of Formation

Although weathering of rocks and primary minerals is the chief source of all salts, salt-affected soils rarely form through accumulation of salts in situ. The major factors responsible for the formation of two principal categories of salt-affected soils are discussed below:

Saline Soils

i. Use of saline groundwater: When groundwater is the only source available for irrigation, high salinity of the irrigation water can cause a build up of salts in the root zone, particularly if the internal drainage of the soils is restricted and leaching, either due to rainfall or applied irrigation, is inadequate.

ii. Saline seeps, are the result of excessive leaching that results from reduced evapotranspiration after a change in land use from a natural forest vegetation to a cereal grain crop or a shift in cropping pattern such as the introduction of a fallow season in a grain farming system. The percolating water passing through saline sediments is intercepted by impermeable horizontal layers and conducted laterally to landscape depressions causing extensive soil salinization.

iii. Salinity problems are also caused by the ingress of sea water through tidal waves, underground aquifers or through wind transport of salt spray. Soluble salts have also been continually exchanged between land and sea - most transfer of salts from the sea taking place through the uplift of marine sediments and exposure on the earth's surface. For soils of semi-arid regions where rainfed agriculture is practised, serious salinity problems can arise if the rainfall is only approximately equal to the evapotranspiration and soluble salts are present in the root zone from either marine deposits or other sources.

iv. Salinity problems are most extensive in the irrigated arid and semi-arid areas. In every river basin, prior to the introduction of irrigation, there exists a water balance between the rainfall on the one hand and stream flow, groundwater level and evaporation and transpiration on the other. This balance is disturbed when large additional quantities of water are artificially spread on the land for agriculture. An important new contribution to groundwater is introduced in the form of seepage from irrigation channels, from irrigation water added over and above the quantities actually utilized for meeting the evapotranspirational needs of crops, and obstructions in the natural drainage brought about by new developments in the area. These new additions to the groundwater will raise the subsoil water level or may form a perched watertable. Studies have shown that once the watertable is within 1 to 2 m of the soil surface, it can contribute significantly to evaporation from the soil surface and therefore to the root zone salinization. Salinization problems can be more severe when the salinity of groundwater is high, as is usually the case in arid regions.

v. Localized redistribution of salts can often cause salinity problems of a significant magnitude. Soluble salts move from areas of higher to lower elevations, from relatively wet to dry areas, from irrigated fields to adjacent unirrigated fields, etc. Salts may also accumulate in areas with restricted natural drainage caused by the construction of roads and rail lines or other developmental activities. Evaporation of stagnant waters may leave considerable amounts of salts on the soil surface.

Sodic Soils

The mechanisms responsible for the formation of sodium carbonate in soils which characterize sodic (alkali) soils have been discussed in several standard works. Groundwater containing carbonate and bicarbonate is one of the chief contributing factors in the formation of sodic soils in many regions. The soils are reported to have formed by desalinization in the absence of enough divalent cations in some parts of the Nile Delta, by high carbonate and bicarbonate water in Wadi Tumilat and by denitrification and sulphate reduction under anaerobic conditions.

Reduction of sulphate ions under anaerobic conditions and in the presence of organic matter was reported to result in the formation of sodium carbonate. According to researchers the alternate wet and dry seasons and the topographic (drainage) conditions appeared to be the contributing factors in the formation of vast areas of sodic soils in the Indo-Gangetic plains of India (Fig. 1.2). During the wet season water containing products of alumino-silicate weathering accumulated in the low lying areas. In the ensuing dry season, as a result of evaporation, the soil solution is concen-trated resulting in some precipitation of the divalent cations, causing an increase in the proportion of sodium ions in the soil solution and on the exchange complex with simultaneous increase in

Fig. 1.2: Extensive areas of sodic lands lying barren

pH. This process repeated over years resulted in the formation of sodic soils.

Researchers pointed out that highly sodic soils could be developed in a closed basin with an excess of evaporation over precipitation if the inflowing water has a positive residual sodicity. Similarly, groundwater containing residual sodicity could result in the formation of sodic soils when the groundwater table is near the surface and contributes substantially to evaporation.

Distribution

There are extensive areas of salt-affected soils on all the continents but their extent and distribution has not been studied in detail. In some countries even the existence of these soils was discovered only through a survey or the pressing demand for agricultural utilization of a region. A first attempt to compile information on the extent of salt-affected soils on a worldwide basis is shown in Table 1.3 is based on this study. Researcher has also presented maps showing the distribution of salt-affected soils in most continents. Any attempt to increase food production in coming years must pay adequate attention to the improvement of existing salt affected soils with little or no production and to prevent further deterioration of productive soils through these degradation processes.

Table 1.3: World Distribution of Salt-affected Areas

Continent	Country	Area, 1 000 ha		Total
		Saline/ Solonchaks	Sodic/ Solonetz	
North America	Canada	264	6 974	7 238
	USA	5 927	2 590	8 517
Mexico & C. America	Cuba	316	-	316
	Mexico	1 649	-	1 649

Continent	Country	Area, 1 000 ha		Total
		Saline/ Solonchaks	Sodic/ Solonetz	
South America	Argentina	32 473	53 139	85 612
	Bolivia	5 233	716	5 949
	Brazil	4 141	362	4 503
	Chile	5 000	3 642	8 642
	Colombia	907	-	907
	Ecuador	387	-	387
	Paraguay	20 008	1 894	21 902
	Peru	21	-	21
	Venezuela	1 240	-	1 240
Africa	Afars and Issas	1 741	-	1 741
	Algeria	3 021	129	3 150
	Angola	440	86	526
	Botswana	5 009	670	5 679
	Chad	2 417	5 850	8 267
	Egypt	7 360	-	7 360
	Ethiopia	10 608	425	11 033
	Gambia	150	-	150
	Ghana	200	118	318
	Guinea	525	-	525
	Guinea-Bissau	194	-	194
	Kenya	4 410	448	4 858
	Liberia	362	44	406
	Libyan Arab Jamahiriya	2 457	-	2 457
	Madagascar	37	1 287	1 324
	Mali	2 770	-	2 770
	Mauritania	640	-	640
	Morocco	1 148	-	1 148
	Namibia	562	1 751	2 313
	Niger	-	1 389	1 389

Continent	Country	Area, 1 000 ha		Total
		Saline/ Solonchaks	Sodic/ Solonetz	
	Nigeria	665	5 837	6 502
	Rhodesia	-	26	26
	Senegal	765	-	765
	Sierra Leone	307	-	307
	Somalia	1 569	4 033	5 602
	Sudan	2 138	2 736	4 874
	Tunisia	990	-	990
	Cameroon	-	671	671
	Tanzania	2 954	583	3 537
	Zaire	53	-	53
	Zambia	-	863	863
South Asia	Afghanistan	3 103	-	3 101
	Bangladesh	2 479	538	3 017
	Burma	634	-	634
	India	23 222	574	23 796
	Iran	26 399	686	27 085
	Iraq	6 726	-	6 726
	Israel	28	-	28
	Jordan	180	-	180
	Kuwait	209	-	209
	Muscat & Oman	290	-	290
	Pakistan	10 456	-	10 456
	Qatar	225	-	225
	Sarawak	1 538	-	1 538
	Saudi Arabia	6 002	-	6 002
	Sri Lanka	200	-	200
	Syrian Arab Rep.	532	-	532
	UAE	1 089	-	1 089
North & Central Asia	China	36 221	437	36 658
	Mongolia	4 070	-	4 070

Continent	Country	Area, 1 000 ha		Total
		Saline/ Solonchaks	Sodic/ Solonetz	
	USSR	51 092	119 628	170 720
South-East Asia	Kampuchea	1 291	-	1 291
	Indonesia	13 213	-	13 213
	Malaysia	3 040	-	3 040
	Vietnam	983	-	983
	Thailand	1 456	-	1 456
Australasia	Australia	17 269	339 971	357 240
	Fiji	90	-	90
	Solomon Islands	238	-	238

2

Basics of Soil

Soils are vital, fragile, finite natural resources that are essential for the sustained production of food and fiber. Soils, however, are subject to degradation and erosion when mismanaged. Between 1950 and 1993, grain area per person worldwide decreased from 0.58 to 0.33 acres (0.23 to 0.13 hectares). As human populations increase, soil resources are used more intensively, with increasing probability that many practices will lead to deterioration of the resource. Competition between agricultural uses and non-agricultural uses of land, such as support of structures, disposal of wastes, and growing plants for recreational and aesthetic purposes will increase.

In ecosystems, soils, water, air, plants, animals and people have interdependent relationships. Soils are dynamic, living systems whose productivity, through management that often includes additions of nutrients, organic materials and water, can be sustained indefinitely. Soils exhibit unique physical and chemical sorptive qualities and dynamics reflective of their inorganic and organic composition. Cycling of carbon, nitrogen and other nutrient elements in nature involves transformations in soils.

Great diversity occurs among soils, sometimes in very small geographical areas, such as building lots in urban areas. The rise and fall of civilizations sometimes has been related to the wise use and misuse of natural resources including soil and water.

Definitions of soil vary, but one view is that the unconsolidated material at the earth's surface becomes soil when biological activity results in a noticeable accumulation of organic matter as revealed by a dark surface colour. Soils that form in loose, fine-grained material weathered from the rock immediately below them are called residual soils. More frequently, soils are formed in materials that have been transported away from the source rock. Examples of such materials are alluvial materials, which have been deposited from running water as in flood plains or deltas; lacustrine material which is deposited in lakes; glacial material which has been moved by ice, and aeolian material which has been transported and deposited by wind.

Many of the intensively used soils in the world are formed in transported materials. Their usefulness often is associated with topography, or with physical and chemical properties inherited directly from the transported material.

SOIL FORMATION

Soils are porous natural bodies composed of inorganic and organic matter. They form by interaction of the earth's crust with atmospheric and biological influences. They are dynamic bodies having properties that reflect the integrated effects of climate (atmosphere) and biotic activity (microorganisms, insects, worms, burrowing animals, plants, etc.) on the unconsolidated remnants of rock at the earth's surface (parent material). These effects are modified by the topography of the landscape and of course continue to take place with the passage of time. Soils formed in parent materials over decades, centuries, or millennia may be lost due to accelerated erosion over a period of years or a few decades.

The exposed surfaces of soils are a common sight on almost any landscape not dominated by rock. The surface of a soil reveals very little about the depth of the soil or its subsurface characteristics. A vertical cross-sectional view of a soil is called a soil profile. Each of the horizontal layers which can be seen in the vertical section is called a soil horizon. Horizons are formed because of the integrated effects of climate and biosphere change and generally become less pronounced with depth. The depth of soils, usually 0.6 to 1.8 m, is determined by the depth to which the mantle material has been altered in a significant way. That part of the three-dimensional soil body in which the effects of climate and biological activity are most pronounced is the soil solum. In succeeding pages the nature and properties of soils, their management, and environmental public policy issues will be discussed.

SOIL COMPOSITION

The proportions of these components may vary between horizons in a soil or between similar horizons in different soils. The ratio of soil water to soil air depends upon whether the soil is wet or dry. The mineral matter, composed of particles ranging in size from the submicroscopic to gravel or even rocks in some cases, accounts for the bulk of the dry weight of the soil and occupies some 40 to 60 per cent of the soil volume. Organic matter, derived from the waste products and remains of plants and animals, occurs in largest amounts in the surface soil, but even here seldom accounts for more than 10 per cent of the dry weight of the soil.

Soils are very porous bodies. Some 40 to 60 per cent of the volume is interparticle space, or pore space. The pores, highly irregular in shape and size but almost all interconnected by passages, contain soil water, soil air, or both of these. The soil water reacts chemically with the soil solids and usually contains dissolved substances and perhaps suspended particles. The soil air approaches equilibrium with atmospheric air through movement of individual gases.

Bedrock is the ultimate source of the inorganic component in soils. When rock is exposed at the surface of the earth's crust, it is broken down into smaller and smaller fragments by physical forces. The fragments may be altered or decomposed by chemical reaction of mineral matter with water and air. Hundreds, thousands, or even millions of years may be required for the weathering or physical and chemical alteration of rock to produce the ultimate end products in soils. Once particles reach a sufficiently small size they can be moved by wind, water or ice when exposed at the surface. It is common, therefore, for small particles to be moved from one location to another. A single particle might occur in several different soils over a period of 100,000 years. Eventually, these particles or their decomposition products reach the ocean where they are redeposited as marine sediments.

The silicate group of minerals is dominant in soil systems. The terms, clay mineral and layer silicate, are used almost inter-changeably. The dominant chemical elements in silicate clays are oxygen, silicon, aluminum and iron. Important constituents in relatively small amounts are potassium, calcium, magnesium and sodium. Other elements occur in very small amounts in silicates. Carbonates, oxides, phosphates and sulfates are other mineral groups that occur commonly in parent materials.

SOIL PHYSICAL PROPERTIES

Soils are porous and open bodies, yet they retain water. They contain mineral particles of many shapes and sizes and organic material which is colloidal (particles so small they remain suspended in water) in character. The solid particles lie in contact one with the other, but they are seldom packed as closely together as possible.

Texture

The size distribution of primary mineral particles, called soil texture, has a strong influence on the properties of a soil. Particles larger than 2 mm in diameter are considered inert. Little attention is paid to them unless they are boulders that interfere with manipulation of the surface soil. Particles smaller than 2 mm in diameter are divided into three broad categories based on size. Particles of 2 to 0.05 mm diameter are called sand; those of 0.05 to 0.002 mm diameter are silt; and the <0.002 mm particles are clay. The texture of soils is usually expressed in terms of the percentages of sand, silt, and clay. To avoid quoting exact percentages, 12 textural classes have been defined. Each class, named to identify the size separate or separates having the dominant impact on properties, includes a range in size distribution that is consistent with a rather narrow range in soil behaviour. The loam textural class contains soils whose properties are controlled equally by clay, silt and sand separates. Such soils tend to exhibit good balance between large and small pores; thus, movement of water, air and roots is easy and water retention is adequate. Soil texture, a stable and an easily determined soil characteristic, can be estimated by feeling and manipulating a moist sample, or it can be determined accurately by laboratory analysis. Soil horizons are sometimes separated on the basis of differences in texture.

Structure

Anyone who has ever made a mud ball knows that soil particles have a tendency to stick together. Attempts to make mud balls out of pure sand can be frustrating experiences because sand particles do not cohere (stick together) as do the finer clay particles. The nature of the arrangement of primary particles into naturally formed secondary particles, called aggregates, is soil structure. A sandy soil may be structureless because each sand grain behaves independently of all others. A compacted clay soil may be structureless because the particles are clumped together in huge massive chunks. In between these extremes, there is the granular structure of surface soils and the blocky structure of subsoils. In some cases subsoils may have platy or columnar types of structure. Structure may be further described in terms of the size and stability of aggregates. Structural class is based on aggregate size, while structural grade is based on aggregate strength. Soil horizons can be differentiated on the basis of structural type, class, or grade.

What causes aggregates to form and what holds them together? Clay particles cohere to each other and adhere to larger particles under the conditions that prevail in most soils. Wetting and drying, freezing and thawing, root and animal activity, and mechanical agitation are involved in the rearranging of particles in soils—including destruction of some aggregates and the bringing together of particles into new aggregate groupings. Organic materials, especially microbial cells and waste products, act to cement aggregates and thus to increase their strength. On the other hand, aggregates may be destroyed by poor tillage practices, compaction, and depletion of soil organic matter. The structure of a soil, therefore, is not stable in the sense that the texture of a soil is stable. Good structure, particularly in fine textured soils, increases total porosity because large pores occur between aggregates, allowing penetration of roots and movement of water and air.

Consistence

Consistence is a description of a soil's physical condition at various moisture contents as evidenced by the behaviour of the soil to mechanical stress or manipulation. Descriptive adjectives such as hard, loose, friable, firm, plastic, and sticky are used for consistence. Soil consistence is of fundamental importance to the engineer who must move the material or compact it efficiently. The consistence of a soil is determined to a large extent by the texture of the soil, but is related also to other properties such as content of organic matter and type of clay minerals.

Colour

The colour of objects, including soils, can be determined by minor components. Generally, moist soils are darker than dry ones and the organic component also makes soils darker. Thus, surface soils tend to be darker than subsoils. Red, yellow and gray hues of subsoils reflect the oxidation and hydration states or iron oxides, which are reflective of predominant aeration and drainage characteristics in subsoil. Red and yellow hues are indicative of good drainage and aeration, critical for activity of aerobic organisms in soils. Mottled zones, splotches of one or more colors in a matrix of different colour, often are indicative of a transition between well drained, aerated zones and poorly drained, poorly aerated ones. Gray hues indicate poor aeration. Soil colour charts have been developed for the quantitative evaluation of colours.

SOIL CHEMICAL PROPERTIES AND CLASSIFICATION

Major Elements

Eight chemical elements comprise the majority of the mineral matter in soils. Of these eight elements, oxygen, a negatively-charged ion (anion) in crystal structures, is the most prevalent on both a weight and volume basis. The next most common elements, all positively-charged ions (cations), in decreasing order are silicon, aluminum, iron, magnesium, calcium, sodium, and potassium. Ions of these elements combine in various ratios to form different minerals. More than eighty other elements also occur in soils and the earth's crust, but in much smaller quantities.

Soils are chemically different from the rocks and minerals from which they are formed in that soils contain less of the water soluble weathering products, calcium, magnesium, sodium, and potassium, and more of the relatively insoluble elements such as iron and aluminum. Old, highly weathered soils normally have high concentrations of aluminum and iron oxides.

The organic fraction of a soil, although usually representing much less than 10 per cent of the soil mass by weight, has a great influence on soil chemical properties. Soil organic matter is composed chiefly of carbon, hydrogen, oxygen, nitrogen and smaller quantities of sulfur and other elements. The organic fraction serves as a reservoir for the plant essential nutrients, nitrogen, phosphorus, and sulfur, increases soil water holding and cation exchange capacities, and enhances soil aggregation and structure.

The most chemically active fraction of soils consists of colloidal clays and organic matter. Colloidal particles are so small (< 0.0002 mm) that they remain suspended in water and exhibit a very large surface area per unit weight. These materials also generally exhibit net negative charge and high adsorptive capacity. Several different silicate clay minerals exist in soils, but all have a layered structure. Montmorillonite, vermiculite, and micaceous clays are examples of 2:1 clays, while kaolinite is a 1:1 clay mineral. Clays having a layer of aluminum oxide (octahedral sheet) sandwiched between two layers of silicon oxide (tetrahedral sheets) are called 2:1 clays. Clays having one tetrahedral sheet bonded to one octahedral sheet are termed 1:1 clays.

Cation Exchange

Silicate clays and organic matter typically possess net negative charge because of cation substitutions in the crystalline structures of clay and the loss of hydrogen cations from functional groups of organic matter. Positively-charged cations are attracted to these negatively-charged particles, just as opposite poles of magnets attract one another. Cation exchange is the ability of soil clays and organic matter to adsorb and exchange cations with those in soil solution (water in soil pore space). A dynamic equilibrium exists between adsorbed cations and those in soil solution. Cation adsorption is reversible if other cations in soil solution are sufficiently concentrated to displace those attracted to the negative charge on clay and organic matter surfaces. The quantity of cation exchange is measured per unit of soil weight and is termed cation exchange capacity. Organic colloids exhibit much greater cation exchange capacity than silicate clays. Various clays also exhibit different exchange capacities. Thus, cation exchange capacity of soils is dependent upon both organic matter content and content and type of silicate clays.

Cation exchange capacity is an important phenomenon for two reasons:

1. exchangeable cations such as calcium, magnesium, and potassium are readily available for plant uptake and
2. cations adsorbed to exchange sites are more resistant to leaching, or downward movement in soils with water.

Movement of cations below the rooting depth of plants is associated with weathering of soils. Greater cation exchange capacities help decrease these losses. Pesticides or organics with positively charged functional groups are also attracted to cation exchange sites and may be removed from the soil solution, making them less subject to loss and potential pollution.

Calcium (Ca^{++}) is normally the predominant exchangeable cation in soils, even in acid, weathered soils. In highly weathered soils, such as oxisols, aluminum (Al^{+3}) may become the dominant exchangeable cation.

The energy of retention of cations on negatively charged exchange sites varies with the particular cation. The order of retention is: aluminum > calcium > magnesium > potassium > sodium > hydrogen. Cations with increasing positive charge and decreasing hydrated size are most tightly held. Calcium ions, for example, can rather easily replace sodium ions from exchange sites. This difference in replaceability is the basis for the application of gypsum ($CaSO_4$) to reclaim sodic soils (those with > 15 per cent of the cation exchange capacity occupied by sodium ions). Sodic soils exhibit poor structural characteristics and low infiltration of water.

The cations of calcium, magnesium, potassium, and sodium produce an alkaline reaction in water and are termed bases or basic cations. Aluminum and hydrogen ions produce acidity in water and are called acidic cations. The percentage of the cation exchange capacity occupied by basic cations is called percent base saturation. The greater the percent base saturation, the higher the soil pH.

Soil pH

Soil pH is probably the most commonly measured soil chemical property and is also one of the more informative. Like the temperature of the human body, soil pH implies certain characteristics that might be associated with a soil. Since pH (the negative log of the hydrogen ion activity in solution) is an inverse, or negative, function, soil pH decreases as hydrogen ion, or acidity, increases in soil solution. Soil pH increases as acidity decreases.

A soil pH of 7 is considered neutral. Soil pH values greater than 7 signify alkaline conditions, whereas those with values less than 7 indicate acidic conditions. Soil pH typically ranges from 4 to 8.5, but can be as low as 2 in materials associated with pyrite oxidation and acid mine drainage. In comparison, the pH of a typical cola soft drink is about 3.

Soil pH has a profound influence on plant growth. Soil pH affects the quantity, activity, and types of micro-organisms in soils which in turn influence decomposition of crop residues, manures, sludges and other organics. It also affects other nutrient transformations and the solubility, or plant availability, of many plant essential nutrients. Phosphorus, for example, is most available in slightly acid to slightly alkaline soils, while all essential micronutrients, except molybdenum, become more available with decreasing pH. Aluminum, manganese, and even iron can become sufficiently soluble at pH < 5.5 to become toxic to plants. Bacteria which are important mediators of numerous nutrient transformation mechanisms in soils generally tend to be most active in slightly acid to alkaline conditions.

SOIL CLASSIFICATION

Soils, like other naturally occurring things, come in great variety and exhibit great ranges of properties. Using measurable and observable properties, such as the kind and arrangement of soil horizons, soils can be characterized and named. The soil series is the lowest category within soil taxonomy (classification system). All soils within a single series have uniform differentiating characteristics and arrangement of horizons. This does not mean that all soils within a series are identical; it does mean that they have the same horizonation, but the horizons may be of different thickness, colour, structure, etc. within prescribed limits. Some 15,000 soil series have been described and named in the United States. Most series names are taken from the name of a town, city, county, river or other constructed or natural feature near the location where the soil is first described and named.

All of the soils within a series will have developed in the same kind of parent material with comparable drainage characteristics and will be of similar age. The effects of climate and biological activity will have been very similar. Consequently, the soils within a series exhibit like properties and respond in like fashion to usage or manipulation.

Higher levels of classification are the family, subgroup, great group, suborder and order. All these categories are given generic names which convey as much information as possible about the soil series to be classified within the group. Eleven soil orders form the highest level of classification. Soils classified within each order show only small differences in the kinds and relative strengths of processes that tend to develop soil horizons.

Considerable effort by soil scientists has been expended, and continues to be expended, in surveying soil resources. These surveys, when done in a detailed manner, require a soil scientist to traverse the landscape at frequent intervals, stopping periodically to auger or dig into the soil. The soil surveyor plots the occurrence of soils on a map which is subsequently formalized and eventually published in a soil survey report which includes not only the soil maps for a given area, usually a county, but all types of information about the county as well as descriptions of the properties of the soils in the area, their present and potential uses, and potential problems associated with the utilization of the soils for both agricultural and engineering purposes. Such reports are very expensive in terms of labour and money, but they contain information that is of great value to those who utilize soils for any purpose. Unfortunately, many who could use the information in soil survey reports to great advantage do not know that the reports are available. With increased emphasis on planning, which includes land use, on county, state and regional bases, more utilization of soil survey information is being made and even more detailed and more modern soil surveys are being urgently requested in many areas. Much of this information is being digitized for electronic transmission.

SOIL ENVIRONMENT

The principal environmental variables affecting life in soils include moisture, temperature, pH, aeration (i.e. presence or absence of sufficient oxygen), organic matter, and inorganic nutrients such as nitrogen and phosphorus. The balance of these factors controls the abundance and activities of the microbes and larger animals in soils which in turn have a marked influence on the critical processes of soil aggregation and degradation of plant and animal residues and the nutrient cycling that accompanies this latter process. To understand life in the soil, the soil is best viewed as an extremely heterogeneous collection of microhabitats. The soil is a matrix of solids including sand, silt, clay, and organic matter particles as well as aggregates of various sizes formed from them, and pore space, which may be filled with air or water. Thus, depending on the mix of environmental variables, prevailing conditions can vary quite markedly over distances on the order of a few millimeters (1 inch = 25.4 millimeters).

Soil Water

Soil water is usually derived from rainfall or some other form of overland flow. The amount of water that enters the soil is a function of soil structure which in turn is a function of texture and higher-order structure i.e. aggregation (e.g. well-aggregated, porous soils allow greater infiltration). Larger pores created by root channels and animal burrows (ant tunnels, crayfish tunnels and worm holes) as well as other types of macropores also greatly facilitate movement of water into and through the soil profile. This is why these soil animals are usually regarded as highly beneficial in soil and why some scientists often use the abundance of earthworms as an indicator of a "healthy soil", though it should be remembered that highly fertile, productive soils do not always contain large numbers of earthworms and other soil animals.

Water moves through soil by mass flow (i.e. fluid movement through larger channels) and by capillary action, the slower movement through the highly tortuous network of very small channels and pores. Most soil water is held in this system of capillary pores and channels and can be held quite firmly through physical interactions with the solid components of the soil matrix. Matric water is held in small (usually microscopic) pores and is often adsorbed onto particle surfaces that can be held rather tightly. Because these interactions with the soil matrix essentially bind the soil water, energy on the part of plants and microbes is required to extract water. These forces are usually given as a matric potential or pressure and they indicate how tightly the water is held. These values are usually expressed as a negative value because they are a measure of the amount of suction required to extract water from the soil. It is this adsorption of water to soil solids that explains why plants can wilt in a soil having substantial clay content, even when some matric water is still present. Beyond a certain point, the water is held too tightly for the plants to extract and the so-called wilting point is reached. An often-stated value for the matric potential at the permanent wilting point is approximately -15 bars (-1.5 mPa). Plants exposed to lower matric (more negative) potentials may wilt and not recover. It should be stressed that the matric potential is a function of soil texture and that fine-textured soils (silts and clays) can contain moisture at very low matric potentials because of the much greater numbers of small particles (greater surface area) and the finer pore network which adsorbs and retains water. Thus in clayey soils, water is not as biologically available as it is in coarser-textured soils. A corollary, however, is that coarse-textured soils do not retain as much water because the larger particles do not adsorb water as well and the larger pores drain more rapidly. Thus, nutrients and other chemicals may be retained in a clay soil whereas they may leach, i.e. move downward, with water more rapidly through sandy soils. These textural concerns are of extreme importance to our understanding of the movement of materials into groundwater.

Water occupying the pore network in soil is often called the soil solution. It is never pure water but rather it is a solution containing dissolved salts and gases. This is the solution which is most available to plants and microbes and provides some of the nutrients needed for growth. Many nutrients actually reach the roots of plants through mass flow of the water to the vicinity of the roots. Too much water in the soil disrupts the ideal balance between air-filled and water-filled pores, i.e. soil aeration (discussed below). Salts dissolved in the soil solution give rise to an osmotic pressure or potential which can be measured. The osmotic potential can influence the movement of water into and out of cells and therefore it is important that the soil solution not be allowed to become too saline (salty) as it might in a soil experiencing increased salinity due to prolonged irrigation and poor drainage. Under low osmotic (high negative) potentials (salty or sugary solutions), water is actually drawn out of cells resulting in physiological impairment, that is, being dehydrated beyond some critical point. This is the basis of preserving foods by adding high concentrations of salt.

Osmotic and matric potentials are the two major factors controlling the availability of water to soil life and of these two, it is the matric potential which most affects soil microbes. As a soil dries, life in the soil must work harder to extract water against ever increasing matric and osmotic potentials. For these reasons, adequate soil moisture is required for maximum rates of plant growth and to maintain the vital soil microbial processes essential for life on earth.

SOIL ATMOSPHERE

The soil atmosphere is the mixture of gases occupying that portion of the pore network that is not filled with water. It is derived from the overlying air but differs in a few prominent ways. Most notably, the soil atmosphere contains less oxygen than the overlying air and typically has 10- to 100-fold more carbon dioxide. You might surmise, and you would be correct, that these changes are driven by the aerobic respiration of the organisms inhabiting the soil. These changes are also a result of the physical characteristics of the soil environment. Generally, the rate of movement of oxygen back into the soil is not sufficient to keep up with all the respiratory demand because movement of gases is restricted by the highly elaborate network of fine pores and capillaries. Filling pores with water restricts the movement of gases even further, and it is for this reason that waterlogged soils often become anaerobic (i.e. depleted of molecular O_2). This condition should be avoided because it gives rise to a number of negative consequences, not the least of which is that plant roots are injured or killed, not just due to lack of O_2, but to the accumulation of toxic products such as organic acids (e.g. acetic acid) or hydrogen sulfide (rotten egg gas) arising from anaerobic activities of soil bacteria.

Most soil organisms are aerobic, i.e. they require O_2 to grow. However, some soil bacteria do not require O_2 and in fact may be killed or inhibited by it. These bacteria are called anaerobes and they function when there are low concentrations of soil O_2, for example, during periods of prolonged waterlogging. Still other bacteria, called facultative anaerobes, can grow in the presence or absence of O_2.

This discussion of soil water and the soil atmosphere reveals why it is so desirable to maintain a soil in a highly aggregated state. Aggregation is indispensable for maintaining the balance between air- and water-filled pores that is essential for the maintenance of aerobic, beneficial microbes and soil animals.

SOIL TEMPERATURE

Soil temperature is controlled by a number of factors not the least of which is the amount of sunlight incident upon it and the amount of water it contains. Soils are warmed by solar radiation. For this reason, dark-coloured soils tend to absorb more heat and warm earlier in the spring than light-colored soils do. Obviously, vegetative cover plays an important role in controlling the amount of solar radiation that reaches the soil surface. We all know the value of a good shade tree on a hot summer afternoon. Because the soil can become quite warm in the surface few centimeters, particularly when free of vegetation, it is not surprising that numbers of microbes and soil animals are lower near the immediate surface. It is frequently just too hot and too dry in this narrow band of soil. Deeper in the solum the soil warms according to its moisture content and the amount of irradiance received on the surface.

Temperature affects soil life in several ways. First, all organisms exhibit preferences for certain temperature ranges; the so-called minimum, maximum and optimum temperatures. Soil microbes can grow across a very wide range of temperatures so that some portion of the population may be active nearly year round. At the lower extremes of temperature (near freezing) are microbes called cryophiles which actually require or prefer these cold temperatures. At the other extreme are thermophiles, organisms which thrive in high-temperature environments like the boiling geothermal hot springs of Yellowstone National Park at temperatures near 94°C (water boils below 100°C because of the lower atmospheric pressure at the higher altitude). Thermophiles are also critical components of composting systems designed to accelerate the conversion of municipal refuse, paper etc. into compost for use in gardens and for disposal onto land. In the middle temperature range (15 to 40°C) we find the mesophiles and, not surprisingly, ourselves (humans) and most other life forms. Most soil microbes are mesophiles. Most of life's important biological processes operate best in the mesophilic range and we find special adaptations in those organisms that live in colder or hotter environments.

Temperature affects soil microbes and microbial processes in another fundamental way. Namely, it governs the rate of chemical and biological reactions. Thus, biological reactions and processes tend to occur more rapidly as temperature rises to some point where some vital function (perhaps an important enzyme) of the cell is impaired or destroyed and the organism is killed. At colder temperatures, reaction rates slow down and may almost com-pletely stop. This is the well-known basis for preserving food from spoilage by keeping it cold in the freezer or refrigerator. We mentioned above that temperature controls biological processes in soil. One can easily see the value of early warming of soils in the spring for germination of seed and an early start of a crop growth cycle. One can also look at maps of soil organic matter content and easily ascertain the combined effects of soil moisture and temperature on maintenance of organic matter in the soil. In warm, moist climates, soil organic matter is difficult to maintain because the conditions for growth of soil microbes are favorable for longer periods of the year. In colder climates, soil organic matter can accumulate because of prolonged periods when the soil is very cold or even frozen in the near surface layers where most microbes reside.

SOIL BIOLOGICAL PROPERTIES

Soil Biota

The soil contains a vast array of life forms ranging from submicroscopic (the viruses), to earthworms, to large burrowing animals such as gophers and ground squirrels. Microscopic life forms in the soil are generally called the "soil microflora" (though strictly speaking, not all are plants in the true sense of the word) and the larger animals are called macrofauna.

Soil animals, especially, the earthworms and some insects tend to affect the soil favorably through their burrowing and feeding activities which tend to improve aeration and drainage through structural modifications of the soil solum. In general, they affect soil chemical properties to a lesser extent though their actions indirectly enhance microbial activities due to creation of a more favourable soil environment.

Soil Microorganisms

Soil microorganisms occur in huge numbers and display an enormous diversity of forms and functions. Major microbial groups in soil are bacteria (including actinomycetes), fungi, algae (including cyanobacteria) and protozoa.

Because of their extremely small cell size (one to several micrometers), enormous numbers of soil microbes can occupy a relatively small volume, hence space is rarely a constraint on soil microbes. Soil microbes can occur in numbers ranging up to several million or more in a gram of fertile soil (a volume approximately that of a red kidney bean). Note that the bacteria are clearly the most numerous of the soil microbes. Perhaps more important than the numbers of the various soils microbes is the microbial biomass contributed by the respective groups. It is the soil fungi which tend to contribute the most biomass among the microbial groups. In fact, it is because of their large contribution to the biomass that they are generally regarded as being the dominant decomposer microbes in the soil. You might find it surprising that there are literally "tons" of microbes beneath your feet as you walk across a grassland in Africa or Australia or through a cornfield in the American Midwest. Interesting-ly, a fungus discovered in the state of Michigan may be one of the largest living organ-isms on the planet.

A fungus, *Armillaria bulbosa*, discovered in the U.S. in the state of Michigan, could turn out to be earth's largest creature or at least among the largest. Scientists discovered the fungus growing among the roots of hardwood trees in a forest. The microscopic, branched filaments (called hyphae) of the fungus occupy a 14.8 ha (37-acre) area of land. Careful genetic analysis has shown the filaments constitute a single organism. Fungi generally radiate outward in a circular pattern as they grow through the soil. In fact, the fairy rings of mushrooms (named because ancient peoples thought they represented the paths of fairies dancing in the night) often seen in lawns or on golf courses actually represent the outer boundary of a developing fungus. Scientists estimate that the portion of the Michigan fungus they have been able to identify may weigh as much as 100 tons, slightly less than a blue whale. Imagine the biochemical capacity of a soil microorganism this large!

The significance of these large amounts of microbial biomass in the soil lies not only in their large biochemical capacity, but in the phenomenal diversity of biochemical reactions attributed to the soil microbial population. It is worth remembering that soil microbes not only interact with other members of their own group, they also interact with other microbial groups. It is quite common to find, for example, that degradation of plant materials occurs much more quickly in the presence of the mixed soil population than it does when one or more groups of soil microbes have been eliminated from the system.

Soil life can be divided into trophic (i.e. feeding) levels. At the base of the trophic levels lies the soil microbial population which degrades plant, animal and microbial bodies, and also serves as the food source for some of the levels above it. For example, soil protozoa consume enormous numbers of bacteria and even some fungal spores. These in turn are consumed by still larger soil animals (nematodes, mites, etc.) which in turn are eaten by still larger animals (e.g. worms and insects). Thus, nutrients flow through this microbial food web which lies at the heart of controlling soil fertility and plant productivity in the absence of external inputs such as fertilizers. In fact, the role of soil microbes in degrading organic materials and thereby regenerating a supply of carbon dioxide for plants is perhaps their most vital global function.

Nutrient Cycling by Soil Microbes

Soil microbes exert much influence in controlling the quantities and forms of various chemical elements found in soil. Most notable are the cycles for carbon, nitrogen, sulfur and phosphorus, all of which are elements important in soil fertility, and as we know today, may be involved in global environmental phenomena. The mineralization (i.e. the conversion of organic forms of the elements to their inorganic forms) of organic materials by soil microbes liberates carbon dioxide, ammonium (which is rapidly converted to nitrate by soil microbes), sulfate, phosphate and inorganic forms of other elements. This is the basis of nutrient cycling in all major ecosystems of the world. We now know that soil microbes accomplish this task with remarkable zeal and that in the process a substantial part (perhaps as much as one-third) of the decomposing materials are converted to the bodies of soil microbes. This pool of microbial biomass constitutes a portion of the soil organic matter which turns over (cycles) fairly quickly and therefore represents a "fertility buffer" in the soil. Don't forget that the liberation of carbon dioxide through microbial respiration makes possible the continued photosynthesis (i.e. carbon dioxide fixation) by algae and green plants which in turn produce more organic materials which may ultimately reach the soil, thereby completing the cycle.

In the world's agricultural soils, the source of our food supply, mineralization of nitrogen by soil microbes is a most important process. In those soils not receiving external inputs of fertilizer nitrogen (e.g. most forested lands and many grasslands) the liberation of ammonium from organic debris makes possible the continued growth of new plant matter. Therefore, it is the soil microbial population which controls the productivity of these soils if other environmental factors (moisture, temperature) are suitable.

In fact, fertilization of a soil represents our attempt to balance the competition between plants and soil microbes for available soil nitrogen. Nitrogen tied-up (assimilated into cell constituents) in microbial cells is not available for plants or other microbes until that tissue has been decomposed by other microbes. In other words, nitrogen contained in tissues is said to be immobilized. Microbes are the keys for the remobilization of these nutrients. These mineralization/immobilization phenomena are common to all the elements but typically they are only agriculturally important for the macronutrients such as nitrogen, phosphorus and sulfur.

Aside from their role in controlling the rates of production of inorganic forms of nitrogen and sulfur, soil microbes, in particular soil bacteria, can control the forms of the ions in which these nutrients occur. For example, ammonium (NH_4^+) in the soil is usually rapidly oxidized by bacteria first to nitrite (NO_2^-) and then to nitrate (NO_3^-) which may readily leach through soil. Ammonium is oxidized to nitrite and then to nitrate by the bacteria *Nitrosomonas* and *Nitrobacter*, respectively. Thus, bacteria can influence the form and, thereby, the retention of nitrogen in the soil. Similarly, reduced sulfur compounds such as thiosulfate, elemental sulfur and even iron pyrite (FeS_2, "Fool's Gold") can be oxidized to sulfuric acid by soil bacteria. The bacteria which accomplish the oxidation of reduced nitrogen and sulfur compounds use these materials as energy sources to drive their metabolism. Unlike the decomposer microbes which use organic carbon compounds from organic matter for energy and to make cell matter (e.g. they are called heterotrophs), these specialized bacteria called chemoautotrophs obtain their carbon for cell synthesis from carbon dioxide or from dissolved carbonate.

There are many genera of bacteria that can oxidize reduced sulfur compounds. However, much of this activity, especially the oxidation of sulfur and pyrite, can be attributed to bacteria of the genus *Thiobacillus* (thio =

sulfur; bacillus = rod-shaped bacterium). *Thiobacillus thiooxidans* can oxidize elemental sulfur to sulfuric acid. Sulfur, therefore, can be used to decrease the pH of an alkaline soil. *Thiobacillus fe*rrooxidans attacks both the iron and sulfur in iron pyrite, generating sulfuric acid and dissolved iron in the process. This is also the basis of acid mine drainage associated with the mining of coal throughout the world.

The long-term application of ammonium-based fertilizers can likewise result in the acidification of agricultural soils through bacterial nitrification (the conversion of ammonium to nitrate with the concurrent production of acidity). Thus, we see that certain environmental problems can arise from the activities of these chemoautotrophic soil bacteria.

Another important aspect of nutrient cycling is that under certain circumstances nitrogen and sulfur may be converted to gaseous forms (volatilized) and lost to the atmosphere. Nitrogen in the form of nitrate can be converted to gases such as nitrous oxide (N_2O) and dinitrogen (N_2) through the process of denitrification (the bacterial reduction of NO_3^- to N_2O or N_2) by soil bacteria under anaerobic conditions. A consequence of denitrification is that nitrogen, a precious nutrient for plants, is lost from the soil. On the other hand, this process is a useful way to remove excess nitrate from wastewater.

Sulfur in the form of sulfate (SO_4^{-2}) is used by anaerobic bacteria like the genus *Desulfovibrio* which convert it to hydrogen sulfide gas (H_2S). Hydrogen sulfide reacts with metal ions and forms very insoluble metallic sulfides like pyrite (Fe_2S). In fact, it is probable that the pyrites associated with coal seams were deposited by the action of these bacteria eons ago. The black colour of salt marsh soils and the rotten egg smell associated with them are a result of the activities of the sulfate-reducing bacteria in these habitats. They attest to the occurrence of anaerobic conditions. Sulfur volatilization from soil represents loss of a plant nutrient as well as a contribution of atmospheric sulfur which may contribute to the phenomenon of acid precipitation.

We mentioned above that nitrogen can be lost from agricultural soils as well as from other ecosystems. Fortunately, this "leak" in the terrestrial nitrogen cycle can be at least partially replaced through another important biological process called biological nitrogen fixation. In this process, which is unique to bacteria and a few other mi-crobes, notably the cyanobacteria (blue-green algae), atmospheric dinitrogen (N_2) is captured and converted to plant-available forms. Biological nitrogen fixation is carried out by free-living bacteria and cyanobacteria and by symbiotic microorganisms in a wide variety of mutualistically symbiotic associations with higher plants.

The most useful and probably the most widely recognized example of symbiotic nitrogen fixation is that of the *Rhizobium* - legume root-nodule symbiosis. Soil bacteria belonging to the genera *Rhizobium* and *Bradyrhizobium* (and a few others) are capable of inducing the formation of nodules on roots of specific legumes (plants like peas, beans, peanuts, soybeans, alfalfa etc.) and fixing large quantities of nitrogen in these structures. In the nodule, the bacteria are supplied with carbon sources (photosynthate from the plant) that they need in order to fix nitrogen. In return for this carbon, the bacteria fix atmospheric nitrogen which is converted to amino acids used by the plant for growth. The result of this unique plant-microbe partnership is that many legumes are self-sufficient for nitrogen, that is, they are nearly independent of a supply of nitrogen from the soil. It is no wonder that these plants are cultivated all over the world as sources of food, fiber and forage. Nearly two-thirds of the world's nitrogen supply is from biological nitrogen fixation. Legumes have been used since the beginning of recorded history as "soil improving" crops known as "green manures".

Green manuring is the practice of growing a legume species for the sole purpose of returning it to the soil to serve as a source of nitrogen for an ensuing crop.

SOIL MICROBES AND BIOREMEDIATION

We have touched on the remarkable metabolic diversity and capacity of the soil microflora. This capacity is increasingly being harnessed and put to good use by humans. A most beneficial spin-off from our understanding of the metabolism of soil microbes has been the development of methods for the bioremediation of soils contaminated by hazardous wastes or spilled petroleum products both on land and sea. Bioremediation may be defined as the controlled use cf microorganisms for the destruction of chemical pollutants. A large number of processes have been developed to handle various wastes and for the cleanup of spilled organic materials. At the heart of all of these processes lies the premise that the metabolic activities of bacteria or fungi can be used to degrade many of the organic chemicals of commerce (solvents, pesticides, hydrocarbon fuels, etc.).

Either of two forms of bioremediation is commonly employed. In biostimulation the environment into which the material has been spilled or otherwise introduced is made favorable for the rapid development of microbes. Typically, this process involves adding sufficient nitrogen and phosphorus fertilizer to overcome nutrient limitations to microbial growth and providing some mechanism for increased aeration of the system. These practices encourage development of the indigenous microbial population which usually contains microbes able to degrade the compounds of interest. In the practice of bioaugmentation, an external microbial population is added in order to speed up the degradation process. Numerous microbes have been developed for such purposes. However, the full measure of the usefulness of such microbial products is not yet known. Some inoculants have reportedly enhanced the remediation process and others have had little or no effect on the process. It is probable that in due time useful microbial products or processes will be developed for use in the clean-up of oil or other chemical spills. What is certain is that successful bioremediation will require detailed knowledge of the factors which make some microbes more competitive than others in a given environment. Only when these details are established will we know how to use sound ecological principles to add microbes to these complex environments to insure their establishment and function in the clean-up process.

PLANT ESSENTIAL NUTRIENTS

Sixteen chemical elements are recognized as being essential for the growth of all plants. Five others, silicon, sodium, cobalt, vanadium, and nickel, have been recognized as necessary for the growth of some plant species. Although certain essential elements can exist in nature in a number of ionic forms, plants can use only specific ones.

Nitrogen

Other than carbon, hydrogen, and oxygen, nitrogen is the nutrient required by plants in the greatest quantity. The nitrogen concentration of plants ranges from about 0.5 to 5 per cent on a dry weight basis. Since most plants have a rather high nitrogen requirement and most soils can't supply sufficient nitrogen to meet this demand, nitrogen normally must be supplemented from organic or inorganic fertilizer sources.

The ultimate source of all nitrogen in soils is the atmosphere, which is approximately 78 per cent N_2. Although this quantity represents an almost unlimited supply, nitrogen as N_2 is not directly available for uptake by most plants. Recall that legumes in symbiosis with particular species of the bacterial genus, *Rhizobium*, transform gaseous N_2 to plant available form, with capacities to fix N_2 ranging from about 40 to greater than 300 lbs N/acre/year. Nonsymbiotic fixation of N_2 by free living soil microorganisms also occurs but quantities are usually less than 10 lbs N/acre/year. Lightning discharge in thunderstorms can oxidize atmospheric N_2 to plant available nitrate, but quantities are generally less than 20 lbs N/acre/year. N_2 can also be transformed to plant available forms through the fertilizer manufacturing process. The chemical triple bond that exists between the two N atoms in N_2 is very strong. All the above processes that convert N_2 to plant useable forms, therefore, are highly energy intensive.

Nitrogen is an extremely reactive element with many of its possible transformations being depicted in the nitrogen cycle. The nitrogen cycle is the dynamic system in which nitrogen is transformed, or cycled, from one form to another. Total nitrogen in the soil-plant-water-atmosphere continuum is conserved, but amounts existing in various "pools", or forms, of nitrogen change with time and environmental conditions. The vast majority of soil nitrogen (approximately 95 per cent) is found in soil organic matter. This organically-combined nitrogen is not immediately plant available, but can be converted to inorganic, available forms through the actions of soil microorganisms. This process, as previously discussed, is termed nitrogen mineralization. Prior to the production of inorganic nitrogen fertilizers, most nitrogen for plant growth was supplied through leguminous N_2 fixation and nitrogen mineralization of added animal manures and indigenous soil organic nitrogen. Sole reliance on nitrogen mineralization from soil organic matter normally is not sufficient for crop production and may result in soil deterioration associated with the loss of organic matter. Nitrogen supplementation, whether from organic or inorganic fertilizer sources, is normally necessary for crop production.

Nitrogen, primarily in the form of nitrate, may be lost from soils through leaching. Nitrate, being an anion, is repelled by the negatively-charged cation exchange sites in soils. Since the ion is not adsorbed and is highly water soluble, it will move downward in soils with percolating water. Nitrate leaching is most common in coarse, sandy soils receiving excess rainfall or irrigation. Nitrate losses may also be increased by applying nitrogen fertilizers, whether inorganic or organic, in excess of a crop's requirement. Nitrate leaching should be prevented not only from economic, but also from environmental and health standpoints. Ingestion of waters high in nitrate has been implicated in gastrointestinal problems in adults and methemoglobinemia ("blue baby syndrome") in infants, though confirmed cases are rare. Near-surface aquifers normally are the most susceptible. Nitrate contamination of waters is usually localized and can be decreased through proper management.

Denitrification is the bacterial reduction of nitrate under anaerobic conditions to N_2 or N_2O gases. Under anaerobic conditions, most nitrate in soils may be denitrified in a period of a few days. Some scientists theorize that atmospheric N_2 is the result of denitrification over geologic time. Evidence also indicates that N_2O may be partially responsible for depletion of the protective ozone layer and is also a potent "greenhouse gas". Thus, loss of nitrate through denitrification not only results in an economic loss of plant available nitrogen, but may also have other detrimental effects. Combustion of fossil fuels also produces nitrous oxides that may contribute to this effect.

Nitrogen is an essential ingredient for the production of sufficient food for an expanding world population. Proper nitrogen management can decrease the potential for negative environmental impacts.

Phosphorus

Phosphorus in soil organic matter accounts for about 20 to 65 per cent of the total phosphorus found in soils.

Therefore, phosphorus mineralization from soil organic matter is an important source of available phosphorus for plant growth. Phosphorous ranks second to nitrogen as a limiting nutrient for plant growth. Although plant available forms of this element are anionic, phosphorus is immobile in soils with appreciable colloid content because it tends to be tightly bound to these tiny particles. Phosphorus may also form water insoluble compounds such as insoluble calcium phosphates in alkaline soils and insoluble iron and aluminum phosphates in acid soils. The concentration of phosphorus in soil solution is normally much less than one part per million (ppm), even in fertilized soils, and often is only hundredths of a ppm in unfertilized soils.

Phosphorus fertilizers are normally produced through acidification of the mineral, apatite, found in high concentrations in some sedimentary deposits. Organic phosphorus sources, such as manure, may also be used. Manures, however, usually contain relatively large quantities of phosphorus relative to nitrogen. Care must be taken with manure additions so that excess phosphorus doesn't result in deficiencies of other nutrients, such as zinc, or contribute to soluble phosphorus in runoff waters.

Soluble phosphorus can be lost in surface runoff waters, but is usually found adsorbed to soil particles transported by erosion. Phosphorus in runoff has been implicated in eutrophication (excessive algal growth) of lakes and streams.

Potassium

Potassium is required by plants in amounts second only to nitrogen. Unlike nitrogen and phosphorus, potassium is not organically combined in soil organic matter. Different potassium-containing minerals, such as micas and feldspars, therefore, are the principal sources of potassium in soils. Clay-sized micas weather more rapidly to release potassium than feldspars because of their much greater surface area. Soils that contain considerable micaceous clays may be able to supply all of a crop's potassium requirement without fertilization. Acid, weathered soils are those most likely to be deficient in available potassium.

Calcium and Magnesium

Calcium is the predominant exchangeable cation in soils, even in the majority of acid soils, followed by magnesium. This occurs because of the large number of minerals in soils that contain calcium and/or magnesium. Actual plant deficiencies of these elements are infrequent because problems associated with soil acidity, such as aluminum toxicity, become limiting first.

Sulfur

Approximately 85 per cent of total soil sulfur is found in soil organic matter. Microbial mineralization of the soil organic fraction is an important source of available sulfur for plant growth. Reactions of sulfur in soils are very similar to those of nitrogen. Sulfides, such as pyrite and other reduced forms of sulfur, are commonly unearthed in metal and coal mining. Upon exposure to oxygen, sulfuric acid which is produced through chemical and biological oxidation can result in soil acidification and acid mine drainage. Soils may also receive sulfur through atmospheric deposition. Soils near large metropolitan areas may receive greater than 150 lbs S/acre/year from the combustion of fossil fuels. Volcanic eruptions can also emit large quantities of sulfur gases. Soils most commonly deficient in available sulfur are sandy, leached soils that are low in organic matter.

Micronutrients

Iron, zinc, manganese, copper, chlorine, boron, and molybdenum are classified as micronutrients. Micronutrients are plant essential elements that are required by plants in much smaller amounts than the other essential nutrients. Generally, less than 1 lb/acre of each micronutrient will be present in the aboveground portion of crops. This small quantity contrasts with the 200 lb/acre or more of nitrogen.

The total quantity of many micronutrients in soils doesn't necessarily relate to plant availability. Most soils, for example, will contain from 20,000 to 200,000 lbs total iron/acre to a depth of six inches, but may not be able to supply a crop with sufficient available iron for uptake of 1 lb/acre. Iron deficiency is usually associated with highly alkaline soils because iron solubility roughly decreases 1000-fold for each one unit increase in soil pH.

Zinc, manganese, and copper availabilities are also decreased by alkalinity and by high organic matter concentrations (> 10 per cent). These three elements form very stable bonds with soil organic matter which decrease their availability.

Plant micronutrient deficiencies are becoming more widespread because of greater quantities required by higher yields and decreasing micronutrient impurities in fertilizers.

SOIL MANAGEMENT

Most soils cannot provide one or more plant essential nutrients in sufficient available form for modern crop production. Soil samples are frequently tested to determine the quantities of nutrients and other amendments which should be applied.

Soil Testing

Soil testing normally involves extraction or reaction of a sample with a specific chemical solution(s) which removes essential elements in amounts related to those required for plant growth. Soil testing is recommended to prevent both under and over fertilization of crops, thereby providing economic crop production in an environmentally effective manner.

Lime

The main purpose of liming is to raise soil pH and supply calcium and sometimes magnesium for plant growth. Other benefits from liming acid soils include increased biotic activity, enhanced mineralization of nutrients from soil organic matter, improved soil structure, decreased potential for aluminum toxicity, and increased availability of other nutrients, especially phosphorus.

Fertilization

A good fertilization program is based on soil testing, especially over several years, so that changes in nutrient availability and other chemical properties can be determined over time. Nutrients can be added in either organic or inorganic forms. Remember that plants utilize only specific ionic forms of the essential nutrients. These specific ionic forms can be provided directly through inorganic fertilizers or indirectly through the decomposition of manures, composts, and other organic amendments. Thus, plant uptake of nutrients should be similar whether initially added through inorganic or organic sources. Additional benefits which may accrue from application of organic materials include improved soil structure and increased water holding and cation exchange capacities. The degree to which these additional benefits occur will be determined by the quantity and quality of organic material applied and its decomposition rate.

Municipal sewage sludge, food processing wastes, and other similar organic wastes are commonly added to soils. Besides the obvious need for disposal, these materials can provide nutrients for plant growth and improve soil properties. Sewage sludges can contain heavy metals, however, especially in industrialized areas. Land application of sewage sludge is usually regulated by state and federal guidelines. When properly utilized, the above materials can be suitable sources of plant nutrients.

Irrigation

Irrigation is practiced to at least a limited extent on each of the earth's continents. Irrigation is a method of at least partially overcoming problems in natural precipitation patterns. These problems may result from an overall lack of precipitation or poor seasonal distribution. Irrigation is normally practiced not only to increase yield, but to provide yield stability. Yields may be increased many fold by irrigation depending on climate and the crop produced. Large scale irrigation projects may also be one facet of an overall program to provide hydroelectric power, flood control, municipal water supplies, and recreation.

Water sources for irrigation include lakes, streams, and groundwater. Numerous water delivery methods are used including furrow, flood, sprinkler, and drip irrigation. Each system is different in efficiency and cost. Both these factors are normally considered before a producer decides on the type of system to be used. Water districts and governmental agencies may also mandate the type of system used based on water quantity, quality, and environmental concerns.

Although development of irrigation capabilities almost immediately increases crop production, long-term effects must also be addressed. Irrigation water must be of reasonable quality (sufficiently low in dissolved salts and of proper ionic composition) to be used for an extended period of years. Many irrigation systems from ancient times through today have failed because of increasing soil salinity over time. Water applied through irrigation is partially transpired by plants or evaporated from the soil. Salts added in the water remain in the soil. Over time, salts can accumulate so as to decrease yields or prevent further crop production.

Providing adequate drainage is also imperative for irrigated lands. Proper drainage not only decreases salt accumulation, but prevents shallow water tables which may restrict plant rooting depth and contribute to upward salt migration during periods of high evaporative demand.

Irrigation has been extremely important throughout the world in providing a stable and abundant food supply, but proper planning and expertise are necessary to sustain economic and environmentally sound irrigated crop production.

Tillage Systems and Conservation Practices

Tillage systems vary widely from conventional, or "clean", tillage where all crop residues are incorporated into the soil with little residue remaining on the soil surface to no-tillage where crop residues are not disturbed and remain on the soil surface from one crop to the next.

Conservation Tillage

Conservation tillage denotes any tillage system in which at least 30 per cent of the soil surface is covered by residue after planting. Tillage is used to destroy weeds, incorporate residues from a previous crop, open the soil surface for increased infiltration and aeration, shatter compacted zones which might restrict root growth, and prepare seedbeds for optimal seed germination.

The principal advantage of conservation tillage is protection of surface soil from water and wind erosion and is frequently used to decrease soil loss on erodible lands. Secondary advantages include increased water storage and organic matter contents. Erosion not only decreases the productivity of soils, but additional economic loss is associated with siltation of reservoirs, dredging of waterways, and removal of particulates to meet drinking water standards. As plant residue cover of the soil surface nears 100 per cent, soil erosion decreases to near zero. Erosional loss can be reduced by more than 80 per cent with a residue cover of 50 per cent. Even a modest residue cover of 10 per cent can reduce erosion by about 30 per cent.

Other alternatives are available for erosion control. Construction of terraces, or berms, which slow and alter the movement of water across slopes has been used for centuries to decrease water erosion. Strip cropping, the planting of alternating strips of crops of different heights or seasonal maturities across a landscape, and contour farming, the production of crops across instead of with slopes, have also historically been used to reduce the erosional forces of wind and water.

Rotation, or planting different crop species, is normally beneficial compared to monoculture, or continual production of the same crop species. Rotation often decreases problems from weeds, disease and insects and may improve soil chemical, physical, and microbiological properties, and crop yield.

Farmers must make many decisions each year. These decisions must result in both economic and environmentally prudent crop production if food production is to be sustainable over the long term.

SOILS AND SOCIETAL ISSUES

An escalating world population will certainly result in increased demand for food, fiber, water, and other natural resources. Only one billion persons are estimated to have lived throughout all history up to the year 1850. Contrast this statistic with an estimated world population of seven billion by the year 2000 and the potential problem becomes more sharply focused. World population is currently doubling about every thirty-five years.

As one of earth's most vital and fragile natural resources, soils come under ever increasing pressure. Quite simply, there is less soil per person with each passing day, making increased productivity per unit of land area a requirement. At the same time there are issues of appropriate land uses, sustainability, environmental protection and water rights.

Land use planning, not popular with persons who value individual rights in use of owned property, is becoming more widespread as more demands are placed on soil and water resources. Further, concern that land retain its productivity over time is increasing. "Wearing out the soils" on a farm and moving on to a virgin territory is no longer the option that it was well into the present century.

An additional land use issue which will take on increasing global importance is urban development. Many of the world's large cities developed where they did because of the stable agricultural production from productive soils in the area. As cities expand, formerly productive agricultural land is covered by highways, housing subdivisions, shopping malls, and other commercial developments. Once appropriated for such uses, these lands cannot economically be returned to agricultural production. Responsible land use planning is expected to become increasingly important in the future.

Organic gardening and farming have attracted much attention in recent years. As emphasized, the organic component in soils has essential roles in determining the soil's physical, chemical and biological behaviour.

Increasingly, decisions that impact use and management of soil resources arise from discussion of problems such as sustainable use of finite resources, water quality, sedimentation in lakes, food quality, endangered species, preservation of wildlife habitats, and cultural practices. Every citizen, through the right to vote, can influence laws that determine how soil and water resources are used and managed. All citizens share the responsibility for ensuring that all natural resources are treated with respect and wisely used. Some citizens must devote their careers to developing still better technology for management and conservation that will ensure continued utility of these precious resources by our successors on planet earth.

SUMMARY

Highlight	Key Terms	Key Concepts
Soil Formation	Dynamic System	Climate, biota, topography, parent material and time interact to form soil
	Soil Profile	Expression of soil forming factors varies with depth; thus soil characteristics change with depth
General Composition	Porous Body	Surface horizons have approxi-mately equal volumes of solids and pores filled with water or air
	Weathering	Weatherable minerals decompose and more resistant minerals of clay size, clay minerals, form
	Transported Materials	Small particles may be transported by water, wind, ice or gravity to form new parent materials for soils
Physical Properties	Soil Texture	Surface area per unit volume of soil, and thus particle size, has profound influence on soil properties, especially reactivity
	Soil Structure	Arrangement of primary particles into secondary units has

Highlight	Key Terms	Key Concepts
		profound influence on porosity and balance between large and small pores
	Soil Consistence	Physical behaviour of soils changes as moisture content changes
	Soil Colour	Soil material that has a reddish hue is well drained; mottled and gray material are poorly aerated
Soil Chemical Properties	Cation Exchange	The ability of soil clays and organic matter to reversibly adsorb and exchange cations with soil solution
	Soil pH	A measure of the acidity or alkalinity of a soil; affects micro-organisms, nutrient availability and plant growth
Soil Classification	Soil Taxonomy	Soils are classified based on presence or absence of diagnostic horizons and other differentiating characteristics
	Soil Series	The six tier system of classification uses words with Greek and Latin origins, except at the series level
	Soil Survey	Maps of soil occurrence on the landscape in relation to its

Highlight	Key Terms	Key Concepts
		classification make possible interpretations for various uses
Soil Environment	Soil Water	Held tightly in micropores. Matric potential, osmotic potential, wilting point. Soil biota must work to obtain water from soil
	Soil Temperature	Soil microbes are widely adapted for life at different temperatures. Thermal preferences for growth. Thermophile, mesophile cryophile.
	Soil Aeration	Waterlogging soil causes shift from aerobic (with O_2) to anaerobic (minus O_2) conditions. Efficiency of microbial processes is usually reduced; toxic substances may accumulate.
Soil Biological Properties	Soil Biota	Includes all life in the soil; macro-fauna (worms, large insects, etc.)
	Soil Microflora	General term to collectively describe the populations of bacteria, fungi, protozoa, algae, etc.
	Microbial Biomass	The total mass of microbes in a soil. An important pool of

Highlight	Key Terms	Key Concepts
		nutrients with short turnover times. Driving force for most of the chemical reactions in soil.
	Nutrient Cycling	Nutrients such as carbon, nitrogen, phosphorus and sulfur are constantly recycled by soil microbes. Important for the continued functioning of earth's ecosystems. Life itself must be recycled.
	Bioremediation	Controlled use of soil microbes for cleanup of oil spills, hazardous chemicals, etc. Relies on the great range of metabolic capacities of soil microbes.
Plant Essential Nutrients	16 Essential Elements	All plants require these 16 chemical elements for proper growth and reproduction.
	Nitrogen Cycle	This dynamic system regulates the transformations and chemical forms of nitrogen in soils; related to plant growth and potential environmental pollution.
Soil Management	Soil Testing	The determination of the plant availability

Highlight	Key Terms	Key Concepts
		of essential nutrients in soils prevents over- and under-application of fertilizers.
	Erosion	Loss of topsoil through the action of wind and water decreases productivity and increases costs from siltation, water purification, etc.
	Tillage	Cultivating soils aids in weed control, aeration, and water infiltration, but can make soils more susceptible to erosion. Conser-vation tillage reduces tillage, leaving crop residues on the soil surface to decrease erosion.
Soils and Societal Issues	Population Growth	Enlarging populations increase the pressure on soil resources for food production.
	Urbanization	Covering soils with highways, houses, and malls permanently removes land from agricultural production.
	Landuse Planning	This concept places greater emphasis on the public good as opposed to private property rights.

3

Basics of Salinity and Sodicity Effects on Soil Physical Properties

INTRODUCTION TO SALINITY AND SODICITY

Saline irrigation water contains dissolved substances known as salts. In much of the arid and semi-arid, most of the salts present in irrigation water are chlorides, sulfates, carbonates, and bicarbonates of calcium magnesium, sodium, and potassium. While salinity can improve soil structure, it can also negatively affect plant growth and crop yields.

Sodicity refers specifically to the amount of sodium present in irrigation water. Irrigating with water that has excess amounts of sodium can adversely impact soil structure, making plant growth difficult. Highly saline and sodic water qualities can cause problems for irrigation, depending on the type and amount of salts present, the soil type being irrigated, the specific plant species and growth stage, and the amount of water able to pass through the root zone.

EFFECTS OF SALINITY ON PLANT GROWTH

Salinity becomes a problem when enough salts accumulate in the root zone to negatively affect plant growth. Excess salts in the root zone hinder plant roots from withdrawing water from surrounding soil. This lowers the amount of water available to the plant, regardless of the amount of water actually in the root zone. For example, when plant growth is compared in two identical soils with the same moisture levels, one soil receiving salty water and the other receiving salt-free water, plants are able to use more water from the soil receiving salt-free water. Although the water is not held tighter to the soil in saline environments, the presence of salt in the water causes plants to exert more energy extracting water from the soil. The main point is that excess salinity in soil water can decrease plant available water and cause plant stress.

Soil water salinity is dependent on soil type, climate, water use and irrigation routines. For example, immediately after the soil is irrigated, plant available water is at its highest and soil water salinity is at its lowest. However, as plants use soil water, the remaining water is held tighter to the soil and becomes progressively more difficult for plants to obtain. As the water is taken up by plants through transpiration or lost to the atmosphere by evaporation, soil water salinity increases because salts become more concentrated in the remaining soil water. Thus, evapotranspiration (ET) between irrigation periods can further increase salinity.

EFFECTS OF SALINITY ON SOIL PHYSICAL PROPERTIES

Soil water salinity can affect soil physical properties by causing fine particles to bind together into aggregates. This process is known as flocculation and is beneficial in terms of soil aeration, root penetration, and root growth. Although increasing soil solution salinity has a positive effect on soil aggregation and stabilization, at high levels salinity can have negative and potentially lethal effects on plants. As a result, salinity cannot be increased to maintain soil structure without considering potential impacts on plant health.

EFFECTS OF SODIUM AND SODICITY ON SOIL PHYSICAL PROPERTIES

Sodium has the opposite effect of salinity on soils. The primary physical processes associated with high sodium concentrations are soil dispersion and clay platelet and aggregate swelling. The forces that bind clay particles together are disrupted when too many large sodium ions come between them. When this separation occurs, the clay particles expand, causing swelling and soil dispersion.

Soil dispersion causes clay particles to plug soil pores, resulting in reduced soil permeability. When soil is repeatedly wetted and dried and clay dispersion occurs, it then reforms and solidifies into almost cement-like soil with little or no structure. The three main problems caused by sodium-induced dispersion are reduced infiltration, reduced hydraulic conductivity, and surface crusting.

Salts that contribute to salinity, such as calcium and magnesium, do not have this effect because they are smaller and tend to cluster closer to clay particles. Calcium and magnesium will generally keep soil flocculated because they compete for the same spaces as sodium to bind to clay particles. Increased amounts of calcium and magnesium can reduce the amount of sodium-induced dispersion.

Infiltration

Soil dispersion hardens soil and blocks water infiltration, making it difficult for plants to establish and grow. The major implications associated with decreased infiltration due to sodium-induced dispersion include reduced plant available water and increased runoff and soil erosion.

Hydraulic Conductivity

Soil dispersion not only reduces the amount of water entering the soil, but also affects hydraulic conductivity of soil. Hydraulic conductivity refers to the rate at which water flows through soil. For instance, soils with well-defined structure will contain a large number of macropores, cracks, and fissures which allow for relatively rapid flow of water through the soil. When sodium-induced soil dispersion causes loss of soil structure, the hydraulic conductivity is also reduced. If water cannot pass through the soil, then the upper layer can become swollen and water logged. This results in anaerobic soils which can reduce or prevent plant growth and decrease organic matter decomposition rates. The decrease in decomposition causes soils to become infertile, black alkali soils.

Surface Crusting

Surface crusting is a characteristic of sodium affected soils. The primary causes of surface crusting are:

1) physical dispersion caused by impact of raindrops or irrigation water, and
2) chemical dispersion, which depends on the ratio of salinity and sodicity of the applied water.

Surface crusting due to rainfall is greatly enhanced by sodium induced clay dispersion. When clay particles disperse within soil water, they plug macropores in surface soil by two means. First, they block avenues for water and roots to move through the soil. Second, they form a cement like surface layer when the soil dries. The hardened upper layer, or surface crust, restricts water infiltration and plant emergence.

RELATIONSHIP BETWEEN SALINITY AND SODICITY AND SOIL PHYSICAL PROPERTIES (EC/SAR)

The relationship between soil salinity and its flocculating effects and sodicity and its dispersive effects influence whether or not soil will stay aggregated or become dispersed under various salinity and sodicity combinations. As irrigation water with low salinity is applied to the soil by irrigation or rainfall, this water flows into the spaces between clay particles (micropores). If salinity of the applied water is low relative to soil salinity, swelling and dispersion of clay particles results. In contrast, irrigation water with higher salinity than the soil tends to cause particles to stay together, maintaining soil structure.

More than fifty years of research have been conducted to determine the relationship between salinity (EC) and sodicity (SAR) of irrigation water and its affects on soil physical properties. This relationship is now understood well enough to make accurate predictions of how specific soils will behave when irrigated water containing different levels of salts and sodium. The main concerns related to the relationship between salinity and sodicity of irrigation water are the effects on soil infiltration rates and hydraulic conductivities.

The Swelling Factor

The ratio of salinity (EC) to sodicity (SAR) determines the effects of salts and sodium on soils. Salinity promotes soil flocculation and sodicity promotes soil dispersion. The combination of salinity and sodicity of soils is measured by the swelling factor, which is the amount a soil is likely to swell with different combinations of salinity and sodicity. Essentially, the swelling factor predicts whether sodium-induced dispersion or salinity-induced flocculation will more greatly affect soil physical properties.

It is possible to draw a line from the sodium content (adjusted ESP) in the left column to the appropriate salt concentration in the right column. The line intersects the middle column, the swelling factor, indicating how much the soil will swell. For instance, drawing a line between adjusted ESP = 2 and an EC = 40 meq/L (red line) yields a swelling factor of 0.0041. In this example, the swelling factor of 0.0041 indicates that dispersion is not a problem. However, a combination of adjusted ESP = 30 and EC = 2 yields a swelling factor of 0.28 which indicates that dispersion is likely. In short, Figure 2 helps show how the dispersive effects of soils with high ESP can be lessened with the flocculating effects of irrigation water with high EC.

Infiltration Rates

Another approach to judging the effects of salinity (EC) and sodicity (SAR) on soil physical properties is to assess potential impacts of various irrigation water qualities on infiltration rates. For example, severe problems are likely if the irrigation water has low salinity and high sodicity. At SAR = 15, a severe reduction in infiltration will occur at an EC = 1 dS/m. An EC of 2.5 or less results in a slight to moderate reduction in infiltration. With an EC greater than 2.5, there will likely not be a reduction in infiltration. Similarly, Table 3.1 numerically defines the relationship between EC, SAR, and infiltration rates.

Table 3.1. Guidelines for Saline-Sodic Water Quality Suitable for Irrigation, presented in Terms of Reduced Infiltration

SAR	EC dS/m No Problem	EC dS/m Slight to moderate	EC dS/m Severe problem
0 to 3	> 0.9	0.9 to 0.2	< 0.2
3 to 6	> 1.3	1.3 to 0.25	< 0.25
6 to 12	>2.0	2.0 to 0.35	< 0.35
12 to 20	> 3.1	3.1 to 0.9	< 0.9
20+	> 5.6	5.6 to 1.8	< 1.8

Factors such as climate, soil type, crop and plant species and management practices also need to be accounted for when determining acceptable levels of salinity and sodicity of irrigation water. Rainfall also plays an important role in the relationship between salinity and sodicity and soil physical properties. Intense rainfall can flush salts beneath the root zone, but often cannot significantly reduce amounts of sodium bound to the soil. Therefore, rainfall can reduce the potential for soil aggregation from salts and increase the likelihood that sodium-induced dispersion will occur.

THE ROLE OF SOIL TEXTURE

Soil texture plays an important role in all aspects of irrigated agriculture, and the role of soil texture with respect to effects of salinity and sodicity is no exception. Soil texture helps determine how much water will be able to pass through the soil, how much water the soil can store, and the ability of sodium to bind to the soil.

Because they are composed of small particles, clay soils can hold more water and are slower to drain than course textured soils. Smaller particles can pack closely together, block the spaces between particles and prevent water from passing through. Sand particles are larger and therefore, have larger pore spaces for water to pass through. Under normal irrigation practices, sandy soils will naturally be able to flush more water through the root zone than clay soils. The end result is that sandy soils can withstand higher salinity irrigation water because more dissolved salts will be removed from the root zone by leaching.

Another important aspect of soil texture has to do with surface area. Because of their tiny size, a given volume of clay particles has far more surface area than the same volume of a larger sized particle. This simply means that clay soils are at a greater risk than course textured soils for excess sodium to bind to them and cause dispersion.

Sands have larger particle sizes, resulting in less surface area; correspondingly, they cannot accept as much sodium as clay particles.

ROLE OF CLAY TYPE

The three main clay types are montmorillonite, illite, and kaolinite clays. On the microscopic scale, each of these clays has a different lattice structure, i.e., different building blocks. This directly affects the ability of sodium to bind to each type. Basically, the more sodium a certain type of clay is able to hold, the more infiltration and hydraulic conductivity will be reduced. Montmorillonite clays are affected by sodium the most, while kaolinite is least affected. This same pattern is also true for the swelling factor. Montmorillonites are the most prone to swelling and dispersion, whereas kaolinites are the least likely to swell and disperse.

4

Salinity and Sodicity

Salinity is the presence of soluble salts in soils or waters. Salinity processes are natural processes closely linked with landscape and soil formation processes. However, human activities can accelerate salinity processes, contributing to long-term land and water degradation. Salinity usually becomes a land use issue when the concentration of salt or sodium adversely affects plant growth (crops, pastures or native vegetation) or degrades soil structure. It becomes a water issue when the potential use of a water is limited by its salt content.

Salt is derived from the weathering of the earth's crust and is transported and deposited in the landscape by hydrologic mechanisms (rainfall and water movement above and below the terrestrial surface). Although the salt content of rainfall is low, rainfall can be the dominant source of salt in some areas. Over millennia, salt has accumulated in areas where water drainage has been very slow, or where shallow watertables occurred during wetter geologic periods.

Because land uses such as agriculture disturb the natural hydrologic equilibrium in a landscape, salinity processes are also affected. Human activities in developing land and water resources can change the hydrologic equilibrium in sensitive areas. Salt problems in agriculture are not new; the decline of civilisations in ancient Mesopotamia has been associated with soil salting under irrigation with rising saline watertables.

Salinity usually develops gradually over an extended period of time. Often, landholders become aware of salinity on their land only after observing a gradual loss of productivity over a number of years. Although salinity can cause production losses, seasonal variability in factors such as rainfall, temperature, solar radiation and incidence of pests and diseases have a much greater effect on yields than salinity in the short term. However, salinity can be an important issue for individual landholders depending on the position of their property in the catchment because substantial proportions of individual properties can be affected.

Sodicity in soil or water is defined as the presence of a high proportion of sodium ions relative to other cations (in exchangeable and/or soluble form). As sodium salts, such as sodium chloride (NaCl), are leached through the soil, some sodium remains in the soil bound to clay particles, displacing other cations such as calcium. A high proportion of exchangeable sodium attached to clay mineral exchange sites weakens the bonds between soil particles when the soil is wetted. As a result, the clay particles swell and often become detached and disperse. The small clay particles move through the soil, clogging the pore spaces.

Sodicity is a condition that degrades soil properties by making the soil more dispersible, restricting water entry and reducing hydraulic conductivity (the ability of the soil to conduct water). These factors limit leaching so that salt accumulates over long periods of time, giving rise to saline subsoils. A soil with increased dispersibility becomes more susceptible to erosion by water and wind.

Sodic soils become dense, cloddy and structureless on drying because natural aggregation is destroyed. The dispersed clay at the soil surface can act as a cement, forming crusts that are relatively dense and hard but typically thin (up to 10 mm thick). The crust impedes seedling emergence and can tear seedling roots as it dries and shrinks. The degree of crusting depends on the soil textural composition, the mineralogy of the clay, the exchangeable sodium content, the energy of raindrop impact, and the rate of drying. Soils with high montmorillonite clay contents will crack on drying.

The genesis of some soils has resulted in sodic subsoils, often with a columnar structure. Sodic subsoils may be dense, with reduced soil water storage, poor aeration and increased soil strength, and can be susceptible to tunnel erosion. Sodicity can also be associated with irrigation water salting or erosion scalding. In this book, the term 'salinity', when used to describe salinity issues in general, usually encompasses sodicity as well.

TYPES OF SALINITY

Primary salinity is salinity that occurs naturally in soils and waters. Secondary salinity refers to salting that results from human activities, usually land development and agriculture. (Salting, also called salinisation, is the process and result of soluble salts accumulating in soils or waters.)

The division between primary and secondary salinity is useful for separating areas where human activities do not appear to be affecting salinity processes (primary salinity) from areas where salinity is clearly influenced by human activities (secondary salinity), frequently associated with quite rapid changes in the environment. However, it is often difficult to categorise salting outbreaks as one or the other type because secondary salinity is often primary salinity accelerated by human activity. Many areas that now exhibit secondary salinity show considerable evidence of having been affected by primary salinity in the past.

Primary salinity appears as naturally occurring saline areas and saline soils. Salt lakes, salt pans, salt marshes and salt flats are all examples of naturally occurring saline areas.

Secondary salinity can be divided into three groups on the basis of the processes contributing to salting:

- Watertable salting is a concentration of salts associated with evaporation of water from a shallow watertable (that is, the upper surface of the groundwater). This process contributes to salinity in both irrigated and dryland (non-irrigated) areas. Seepage salting is a type of watertable salting that occurs when groundwater seeps at the ground surface.
- Irrigation water salting is salting associated with the accumulation of salts from irrigation water in the soil and the effect of the water composition on soil properties. The sodicity of irrigation water and the properties of irrigated soils are important components of irrigation water salting.
- Erosion scalding is salting primarily caused by erosion processes. This occurs when surface soils are eroded by surface water flow or wind, exposing saline and/or sodic subsoils.

WATERTABLE SALTING

Appearance

Salting associated with a rising or shallow watertable can become apparent in the following ways:

- The ground surface may become permanently or seasonally damp or waterlogged, or remain damp for extended periods after rain. Previously ephemeral gullies and streamlines may begin to flow continuously or for longer periods.

- Vegetation in low-lying areas may fail to germinate or grow, or may die off over a period of time.
- Pasture composition and diversity may change over time so that couch grass or other salt-tolerant species dominate.
- In residential areas, buildings may suffer from rising damp.
- Groundwater quality may deteriorate.

An area severely affected by watertable salting typically consists of a bare area, perhaps with a salt-encrusted soil surface, fringed by salt-tolerant vegetation, with groundwater underlying or seeping through the soil surface. In a seepage area, the ground will appear wet or shiny. If the salting is not severe, the seepage area itself may be lightly vegetated with salt- and water-tolerant species but the surrounding area may be bare. In some situations, the groundwater does not rise near the soil surface because a deep creek or gully in the vicinity intersects the watertable and acts as a drain. The base flow in such a drain may be poor quality, saline water.

Process

Watertable salting occurs when the watertable exists close to the soil surface. Capillary action draws water from the watertable upwards through the soil. This water evaporates or is used by vegetation. Salts which were dissolved in the water accumulate at the soil surface or in the root zone when the water is removed. Salt concentration can increase to a level at which vegetation can no longer survive.

Seepage salting, a form of watertable salting, occurs when the watertable is at the soil surface, permanently or seasonally, and groundwater seeps through the soil surface. A seepage can reduce salt accumulation in the soil by moving salt to the soil surface and flushing it away. However, salt can accumulate in the area surrounding a seepage as a result of capillary action from the shallow watertable.

Where watertable salting occurs, the groundwater itself is often, but not necessarily, saline. Watertable salting can occur in irrigated areas as well as dryland areas. When groundwaters are used for irrigation, watertable rise is rarely a problem because there is no net increase in the amount of water entering the catchment; excess water draining below the root zone is effectively cycled from the groundwater to the irrigation water and back to the groundwater. Watertable rise is more likely to occur when surface waters are used for irrigation because this increases the water inputs to the system—amounting to a 200 to 600 mm/yr effective increase in rainfall, doubling rainfall input in some irrigation areas.

In dryland areas, watertable salting usually occurs after vegetation clearing and subsequent development reduces water use and thus the ability of the system to maintain the watertable at an adequate depth below the soil surface.

IRRIGATION WATER SALTING

Appearance

In irrigated areas, the effect of irrigation water quality on soil behaviour and plant growth may be apparent as:

- Crop yields may decline progressively over a number of years or be significantly reduced in dry years.
- In severely affected areas, soils may appear 'fluffy' and light (characteristic of saline soils). The soil

surface may be dispersible, water infiltration limited, the seedbed poor, and germination poor or unsuccessful (characteristic of sodic soils).

- Crops may appear water-stressed even though adequate amounts of water have been applied.

Process

Irrigation water salting and sodicity occur when salts (including sodium) from irrigation waters accumulate in soils. This is caused by the two interacting processes of salt accumulation and insufficient leaching:

- All natural waters contain salt. Salt from irrigation waters accumulates in irrigated soils as the water is removed by evaporation and transpiration. Poor quality irrigation waters contribute comparatively greater amounts of salt.
- Leaching moves salt below the root zone. Under certain soil conditions or water management practices, and where sodicity is a problem, leaching rates may not be sufficient to maintain salt in the root zone below a concentration at which plant productivity is affected.

Under irrigation, salts leached from the root zone tend to move downwards into the groundwater. In groundwater irrigation schemes, the salt concentration of the groundwater supply may increase, contributing greater amounts of salt to the soil over long time periods (decades).

Irrigation water salting can be partly controlled by growing salt-tolerant crops and by fine-tuning irrigation management. Where irrigation is used only to supplement rainfall, salinity is of less concern than sodicity; the soil salt concentration can be reduced dramatically by wet season rainfall but the proportion of sodium ions in the soil will remain high or increase slightly.

EROSION SCALDING

Appearance

Areas affected by erosion in conjunction with high salinity or sodicity may appear as follows:

- Midslope and flat areas may become bare of vegetation or support only stunted vegetation growth.
- The soil surface in some areas may be hard and compacted when dry or eroded.
- Pasture composition may change and diversity decrease over time.

In general, the ground in a scald will be bare or may be partially covered by drought- or salt-tolerant species or stunted vegetation. Usually, the soil surface will appear hard and compacted. If stones are present in the subsoil, the eroded surface may have a stonepacked appearance. If the subsoils are strongly saline, salt crystals may be apparent on the soil surface. High subsoil sodicity is a dominant features of scalds.

Areas surrounding scalds can also be affected by the process contributing to the scalding—that is, erosion and deposition of eroded material.

Process

The process of scalding usually begins when vegetation is removed—whether by clearing or overgrazing or by drought or fire. Without vegetation to bind the soil and provide a protective cover, wind and water erosion remove the topsoil, exposing the subsoil. A dispersed surface (crust) forms on the surface of the subsoil.

This crust inhibits vegetation growth, increases runoff and contributes to poor soil structure. The dispersed surface is made up of (mostly fine) sand, silt and enough sodic clay to cement it together when dry and seal the surface. The crust disperses when wet.

SOURCES OF SALT

The dominant sources of salt are rainfall and rock weathering. Rain is a dilute source of salt, but over time, salt deposited by rain can accumulate in the landscape. Rainfall contributes salt to the landscape at about two to three times the 'average' rate that weathering contributes salt, based on some broad estimates. However, weathering can be a dominant source of salt in some landscapes. The dominant source of salts in a particular area will depend on the rock types and the extent of weathering.

Rainfall patterns and soil properties determine the extent to which weathering products remain in the soil profile. In areas with high rainfall and good drainage, most of the salt produced by weathering is flushed out of the landscape. The converse is true, and particularly so, in more arid areas where rainfall is insufficient to leach salt and where drainage out of the region is restricted, such as in Lake Eyre.

Where rainfall is the dominant source of salt, sodium chloride is the most common salt. Where weathering dominates, bicarbonate salts are more common.

RAINFALL

The concentration of salt in rainfall is greatest near the coast, and decreases inland as distance from the coast increases. Salt accessions from rainfall are greater in southern latitudes than in northern latitudes. For instance, the salt concentration of rainfall near the coast north of 24°S is about one-tenth of the concentration of salt in rainfall near the coast in latitudes south of 30°S.

Differences in sea surface salinity combined with wind patterns and intensities may explain this latitude effect. Variations in sea surface salinities, which depend on relative precipitation and evaporation rates, are minor in Australian oceanic regions (less than 2 000 mg/L).

WEATHERING

All weathered rock types contribute salts to the landscape to differing extents. For instance, marine sediments contain greater amounts of salt than freshwater sediments, and contribute more salt on weathering. The texture of sediments influences the extent to which salt is retained during weathering. The salts derived from marine sediments are mainly sodium and magnesium chlorides.

ENVIRONMENTAL FEATURES CONTRIBUTING TO SALINITY RISK

The interaction of processes contributing salt (rainfall and weathering), combined with the influence of other climatic and landscape features and the effects of human activities, determine where salt is likely to accumulate in the landscape.

The factors contributing to salting in differ to a degree from those occurring in other Australian States. These differences should be taken into account if information on salinity processes and management options is to be applied in other areas and climates.

Climate and Rainfall Patterns

Seasonal rainfall/evaporation patterns In general, the most severe watertable salting occurs in areas where most seasonal rain falls in winter. The greatest incidence of watertable salting occurs in coastal areas to the south, where rainfall is less summer-dominant than in the north. The degree of summer rainfall dominance decreases from the north-east to the south-west of the State.

Areas receiving winter-dominant rainfall experience greater recharge to groundwater (and likelihood of watertable rise) than areas receiving summerdominant rainfall. Winter rainfall occurs during a period of low evaporative demand, so there is an excess of rainfall over evaporation. In addition, the rainfall is usually of relatively low intensity, compatible with soil infiltration rates. These factors result in a net water surplus so that water moves below the root zone to the watertable.This also results in greater leaching of salts into the groundwater.

In contrast, summer-dominant rainfall occurs during the active growth period when plant demand and evaporation rates are both high. Summer rainfall is usually of higher intensity with proportionally greater runoff. As a result, a much smaller proportion of water moves below the root zone as deep drainage than in winter-rainfall areas, reducing the likelihood of watertable rise. In some areas in subtropical and tropical coastal, rainfall exceeds evapotranspiration due to the volume of rainfall during the wet season.

Water balance modelling for winter- and summer-dominant rainfall regimes indicates that recharge is an annual event in winter rainfall climates. In contrast, recharge tends to be episodic in summer-rainfall climates, and the effect on salinity depends on the time distribution of rainfall events.

Average annual rainfall is a useful indicator of salinity risk. Annual rainfall ranges from more than 4000 mm/yr in the coastal tropics to less than 200 mm/yr in the south-west near Birdsville. In general, areas receiving on average more than 700 mm/yr and less than 1100 mm/yr are at the highest risk of watertable salting. Areas receiving less than 600 mm/yr are not usually at risk of salinity because insufficient rain falls to satisfy plant demand and recharge the ground-water. Similarly, areas receiving more than 1500 mm/yr are also considered to be low risk because the higher rainfall leaches salt through the soil profile. In the intermediate rainfall ranges (600 to 700, 1000 to 1500), salinity risk is moderate.

Long-term Rainfall Trends

Areas affected by watertable salting can fluctuate in size and severity in response to long-term rainfall trends. When annual rainfalls are consistently above average for a number of years, this has a cumulative effect on groundwater recharge and the likelihood of watertable rise increases. During these periods, areas affected by recurrent waterlogging will usually be at maximum size and severity. In such areas, a series of dry years can lower watertables, greatly reducing the rate of salt accumulation that results from evaporative concentration.

Many salinity outbreaks are first noted after periods of above average rainfall. For instance, salinity outbreaks on the Darling Downs were noted in the early 1950s following an extended wet period. With normal climatic fluctuations between drought and wet periods, salting may become apparent in susceptible areas 20 to 50 years after clearing. In irrigation areas, salting can develop in much less time because of the greater input of water.

LANDSCAPE CHARACTERISTICS

Landform Features

Watertable salting commonly occurs upslope of landscape features that restrict or inhibit groundwater movement or that provide preferential flow paths to the ground surface.

For instance:

- Geological features, such as faults or dykes, create barriers to water flow so that groundwater accumulates upslope of these barriers.
- Heavy soils at the base of slopes or clays deposited at the confluence of streams slow the movement of water through the soil or sediments, resulting in watertable rises.

- When water flowing through relatively permeable rock types or sediments encounters less permeable underlying materials, the water flows along the line of the stratum rather than through it.
- Where rock bars or other barriers constrict the throat of a catchment, the rate of groundwater flow is reduced and water pools upslope of this point.

Human-constructed barriers to water flow, such as roads or dams, have a similar effect.

Historic Salt Loads

During the period of landscape and soil formation, salinity processes caused salt to accumulate in areas where drainage was poor or where watertables were close to the soil surface. As more recent climates have been drier than past climates and watertables deeper, these historic salt loads are now generally at some depth in undisturbed landscapes.

When the hydrologic balance of a landscape is changed through natural processes or human activities so that a new and wetter hydrologic equilibrium is established, rising watertables can move salt from these historic salt loads closer to the soil surface.

Most occurrences of watertable salting can be attributed to the mobilisa-tion of historic salt loads following land development. Vegetation patterns and soil morphological properties, such as inclusions of calcium carbonate, silcrete, ironstone, or manganese–ironstone nodules formed during extended periods of wetness in the past, are often evident in these areas.

Human activities

In areas sensitive to hydrologic change, watertable salting can occur when human activities disturb the hydrologic balance by increasing water inputs to the catchment or by introducing barriers to water movement within the catchment.

There is a marked association between land clearing and outbreaks of watertable salting in hydrologically restricted catchments, although there can be long time intervals between clearing and salting. This delay depends on the degree of hydrologic change (due to clearing, irrigation, climatic variation) and the storage and outflow capacities of the catchment. Finely balanced catchments with low storage and subsurface outflow capacities will experience salting in perhaps a few years compared with a number of years in catchments with greater capacities.

When native vegetation is cleared and an area is developed for agriculture, grazing pressure and cropping practices can reduce the vegetative cover at times such that the vegetation cannot adequately use the available water provided by rainfall. Also, most crop and pasture species are more shallow-rooted than native species. During these periods, extra water moves below the root zone to the groundwater, increasing the likelihood of watertable rise. Clearing in the Lockyer Valley in the early 1900s first resulted in salinity about 30 years later, which increased markedly in the 1950s before establishing an apparent equilibrium in the 1960s. Similarly, salinity developed on cleared areas in the Bundaberg Irrigation Area approximately 35 years after initial clearing.

The use of reticulated water supplies in unsewered rural residential areas can, in effect, increase the rainfall to a landscape, disturbing the hydrology to such an extent that extensive waterlogged or saline areas develop. Landscapes under unsewered rural residential developments can receive an equivalent increase in rainfall of about 100 mm/yr (based on residential water supply design guidelines). Surface water irrigation can contribute water inputs equivalent to an increase in annual rainfall of some 200 to 600 mm/yr. Depending on their position and construction, roads and dams can act as barriers to water movement. Shallow watertables and seepage areas can develop upslope of some roads and dams.

DIAGNOSING SALINE AND SODIC SOIL PROBLEMS

Definitions

- Basic - High pH. Problems usually start at < 7.8 (alkaline).
- Saline - High salt content.
- Sodic - High sodium content.
- Saline/sodic - High salt and high sodium content.

In-field Diagnosis

Visual symptoms can be used to identify these problems, but ultimately a soil test is the best way for an accurate diagnosis. When salinity is suspected from a high water table, you may be able to measure groundwater depth by boring holes with an auger. If free water collects in holes less than 4 to 5 feet deep, a drainage problem is indicated.

Normally, high pH or basic soil doesn't look different than soil with neutral pH, although sometimes the soil may have a powdery substance on the surface. Plants growing in these soils sometimes give clues about the problem. High pH reduces the availability of some nutrients (zinc, iron, phosphorus). Signs of high soil pH include yellow stripes on middle to upper leaves (signs of zinc and iron deficiency); or dark green or purple coloring of the lower leaves and stems (signs of phosphorus deficiency). Looking for symptoms is useful when growing high pH sensitive plants such as dry beans, sorghum, or silver maples. Corn and wheat are moderately susceptible to high pH and may also suffer from nutrient deficiencies on these soils.

Plants growing in saline soils may appear water stressed. This is because the high salt content of the soil hampers the ability of plants to take up water from the soil. Water naturally moves from areas of low salt content to high salt content. Sometimes a white crust is visible on a saline soil surface. Plants that are sprinkler irrigated with saline water often show symptoms of leaf burn, particularly on young foliage.

If a soil is sodic, a brownish-black crust sometimes forms on the surface due to dispersion of soil organic matter. Dispersion of soil particles also results in crusting and impaired drainage. Often you will first notice reduced seedling emergence and viability. By the time darkened crusts are visible on the soil surface, the problem is severe and plant growth and soil quality are significantly impacted. Laboratory analysis of soil is the best way to diagnose these problems before plant growth is severely damaged.

Laboratory Diagnosis

Soil testing labs typically evaluate pH and EC (electrical conductivity) as part of a routine analysis. If the pH is high (<8.5), sodium adsorption ratio (SAR) should also be calculated. See Table 4.1 to evaluate the lab results.

Table 4.1. Classification of salt-affected soils

Classification	Electrical conductivity (dS/m)[1]	Soil pH	Sodium adsorption ratio (SAR)[2]	Soil physical condition
Slightly Saline	2 - 4	<8.5	<13	normal
Saline	>4.0	<8.5	<13	normal
Sodic	<4.0	>8.5	>13	poor
Saline-Sodic	>4.0	<8.5	>13	varies
High pH	<4.0	>7.8	<13	varies

1. dS/m = mmho/cm
2. If reported as exchangeable sodium percentage (ESP) use 15% as threshold value.

If you suspect salinity or sodicity problems, collect a soil sample from the top 6 to 12 inches of soil, concentrating on the areas that appear most impacted. High pH, salt or sodium levels are rarely uniformly distributed across fields. Areas of the field suspected of these problems should be mapped and sampled separately to fully understand the severity of the problem. Be sure to tell the laboratory that you suspect a problem and ask that they analyze for SAR or exchangeable sodium percentage (ESP) and perform a gypsum test, if necessary.

If you are irrigating the site in question, collect a water sample for analysis as well. High levels of salts and sodium may come from irrigation, a high water table, manure or fertilizer inputs, or from the soil parent material. To effectively manage the problem, you need to know the source of the salts. Although 4.0 dS/m is used as a general threshold EC to define saline soils, many sensitive crops such as some vegetables and ornamentals will show symptoms and reduced yields at ECs of 2-4 dS/m.

5

Hydrologic Controls on Salinity

Water is the dominant medium for salt movement in the environment. When water is removed from the environment by processes that exclude salt, such as evaporation and transpiration, salt is deposited and accumulates over time.

Evaporation occurs at the soil/atmosphere interface where groundwater seeps at the soil surface or where the watertable is close enough to the soil surface for capillary action to draw water to the surface. Another source of salt accumulation is evaporation of surface water. This is important in areas where salt is not regularly flushed out of the catchment.

Transpiration occurs at the soil/root interface where plants absorb water from the soil, generally excluding salts dissolved in the water so that these salts accumulate in the root zone. When vegetation has root systems reaching to a deep watertable, salt accumulates at greater depths in the soil profile or over a larger depth range above the watertable.

Hydrologic equilibrium results from a balance between climate (largely rainfall and temperature) and the development of a landscape (including weathering/soil formation and vegetation pattern).

The presence of a discharge area indicates that the rate of water movement into the groundwater of the catchment exceeds the rate of water movement out of the catchment. Thus, only hydrologically sensitive catchments (without effective vegetative or soil water storage buffers) will exhibit waterlogged or saline discharge areas.

Soil hydraulic properties govern the height to which the capillary fringe of the watertable can rise within a given soil. When the capillary fringe intersects the soil surface, soil hydraulic properties also determine the maximum rate at which groundwater and dissolved salts can be transported to the soil surface. If the daily evaporation rate exceeds the supply of groundwater to the soil surface, the soil dries and capillary rise is greatly reduced.

In undisturbed areas, the native vegetation is generally in equilibrium with the natural hydrology of an area. Trees normally utilise all the available water and remove water from the area by evapotranspiration. A small proportion of rainfall (less than 10%) evaporates from the surfaces of grasses and the leaves of trees. In this situation, the vegetation is able to cope with and moderate the effects of variations in seasonal and yearly rainfall.

When trees are removed, water usage in the system generally decreases, runoff slightly increases, and the resulting excess water may percolate through soils and weathered rock into the watertable. If lateral drainage is poor, the level of the watertable will rise, establishing a new hydrologic balance in the system. The salinity of the groundwater may increase as additional salt is dissolved from weathered rocks and soils not previously below the watertable.

Thus vegetation provides a buffer in the system, with the capacity to utilise the available water in the landscape. There are limits: if rainfall is so low that plants cannot grow or reproduce (for example, the Sahara Desert and to a lesser extent the Simpson Desert), vegetation will be limited or absent; if rainfall is so great that it exceeds the ability of any vegetation to utilise the water (that is, the rainfall exceeds the potential evapotranspiration capacity of plants which is determined by the radiation energy), there will be an excess of water. In the second case, the landscape adjusts to the extra water through geomorphological processes such as enhanced weathering, erosion, gully formation, and increased baseflow in streams.

GROUNDWATER MOVEMENT MODEL

The spatial distance between areas where recharge and discharge occurs will vary from catchment to catchment. In some cases, these areas may overlap; in others, the recharge and discharge areas may be separated by thousands of kilometres.

Recharge

Recharge is the process of water entering the groundwater. Recharge areas are areas where the net movement of water is into the groundwater. Relatively permeable areas of the landscape, usually on the upper slopes and on shallow soils, act as recharge areas.

The critical parameters in determining the rate of recharge are soil properties and depth, rainfall and evaporation patterns, and vegetation type. Soil properties influencing recharge include:

- characteristics of the macropores, which transport water to the groundwater when the soil is saturated
- the drainable porosity of the soil, which is the capacity of the soil to release water between

saturation and the point where water ceases to drain readily (field capacity)

- plant available water capacity, which is the capacity of the soil to retain water between an upper limit determined by the field capacity and a lower limit when water becomes unavailable to plants (wilting point).

The effectiveness of vegetation in exploiting available soil water, particularly at depth, varies depending on factors such as growing season, rooting depth, drought tolerance, and vegetation density.

Recharge is maximised where:

- soils are shallow overlying fractured rocks
- soils are highly permeable, or outcrops of fractured rock occur
- vegetation is shallow-rooted or absent
- the rainfall pattern is characterised by rainfall in excess of evapotranspiration for a period of the year.

The depth to the watertable in a recharge area is usually considerable. Watertable level tends to respond quickly to rainfall with marked seasonal fluctuations.

Transmission

Transmission areas occur where the dominant movement of water within the groundwater is approximately parallel to rather than toward or away from the soil surface. Transmission areas generally occur in areas of intermediate and decreasing slope.

Soils are deeper and less permeable than those in recharge areas.

The depth to the watertable in transmission zones is usually less than in recharge areas, with less marked seasonal fluctuations.

Discharge

Discharge areas are areas where the net movement of water is upwards/outwards from the ground. They generally occur where there is some hydrologic restriction to downslope water transmission, causing water to flow toward the soil surface where it 'discharges' from the groundwater. Discharge areas often occur where the ground is flat or poorly incised. In a range of landscape types that are particularly susceptible to watertable salting, discharge areas occur in characteristic positions in the landscape. Soils in discharge areas are generally deeper and less permeable (because of higher clay content) than in recharge and transmission areas. This is because past weathering products of upslope areas accumulate in discharge areas.

The watertable in a discharge area is usually at or near the soil surface, with subdued seasonal fluctuations compared with recharge and transmission areas. Waterlogging and salinity usually manifest in discharge areas. Salt accumulates when water is removed by evaporation and transpiration and salt is left behind. However, land use changes and landscape features in recharge, transmission and discharge areas will determine the extent and severity of salting in discharge areas.

During rainfall periods, surface salt accumulations in discharge areas are leached downwards into the root zone, particularly if the watertable is low following a number of drier than average years. During a subsequent wetter than average cycle, salt accumulated in the root zone will be moved upwards by the rising watertable. Thus, through a series of wet and dry cycles, salts continue to accumulate in the soils and groundwater in discharge areas.

The form of salting in a discharge area depends on the rate of upward water movement to the soil surface compared with the rate of evaporation at the soil surface. Three situations can result:

- If water moves upward through the soil more quickly than it evaporates at the soil surface (rate of water rise exceeds evaporation rate), a seepage will develop. The salinity of the seepage will depend on the salinity of the groundwater.
- If the capillary fringe of a shallow watertable moves water to the soil surface at approximately the same rate as evaporation removes water from the soil surface, salt will accumulate on the soil surface at the maximum rate. Salt will be more concentrated in this situation than in the case of a permanent or seasonal seepage, which would allow any accumulated salt to be periodically flushed away.
- If water evaporates from the soil surface more quickly than it moves upward through the soil and if the watertable is deep enough that capillary rise to the soil surface is not significant, vegetation may maintain the area in hydraulic balance without any salt concentration at the soil surface. However, salt will accumulate in the root zone as plant roots continue to take up water and exclude salt. The magnitude of this accumulation will depend on the salinity of the groundwater and the extent to which rainfall flushes salt away from the soil surface or leaches salt through the soil.

On the basis of current experience, areas where the watertable is less than 6 metres deep under undisturbed vegetation have the greatest potential to develop watertable salting when subject to clearing or other land development. Deeply incised creeks can prevent watertable rise, but these do not usually occur in areas susceptible to salting.

Groundwater encountered in topographic positions above valley floors is usually associated with perched watertables. These form when downward percolating water (from rainfall and runoff) is held up by impermeable layers in the weathered zone. The water in the perched water body may slowly percolate through the barrier into the deeper regional groundwater and/or move laterally to toeslopes and/or be used by vegetation through evapotranspiration.

Water in a perched water body builds up following significant rainfall events, and may be present for weeks or a few months. Irrigation can produce perched watertables in a similar manner.

Discharge is maximised where:

- the watertable is at or very close to the soil surface (salt accumulation is generally greatest when the watertable is permanently between 0.5 and 1.5 metres below the soil surface)
- the soil surface is bare or sparsely vegetated
- soil properties at the site allow a maximum rate of water movement through the surface layers.

SALT MASS BALANCE

Salt mass balance refers to an equilibrium between salt entering and salt leaving the catchment. For instance, salt entering the catchment in the form of a large volume of water with low salt concentration, such as rainfall, can be in balance with salt leaving the catchment as a trickle of outflow of very high salt concentration. The accession of salts from weathering and rainfall and the export of salts through stream flow and groundwater discharge are in equilibrium. In periods of adjustment between changing inputs or outputs, there will be a change in the salt storage in the landscape until the new equilibrium is attained. The salt storage may increase or decrease or, most commonly, salt mobilisation will cause a translocation of salt within the existing storage.

This is described by the steady state mass balance equation:

$$Q_i c_i = Q_o c_o \quad (5.1)$$

where

Q_i is quantity of water entering the system

c_i is salt concentration of the water entering the system

Q_o is quantity of water leaving the system

c_o is salt concentration of the water leaving the system.

Typical Values

Ranges of values that can be expected in salt mass balances have been compiled using information from salt-affected catchments in these areas. The catchments from which this information was gathered received summerdominant rainfall of between 600 and 1000 mm/yr with class A pan evaporation of around 2000 mm/yr.

Three processes stand out as contributing to salting: the mobilisation of historic salt, evaporation and transpiration. The mobilisation of historic salt can contribute 50 to 100 times more salt than rainfall. Evaporation from the soil surface and evapotranspiration by vegetation are significant processes concentrating salt as well as removing water from the catchment.

RATE OF WATER MOVEMENT IN THE LANDSCAPE

The rate at which water moves through porous materials (soils or aquifers) in the landscape depends on the hydraulic conductivity of the material through which the water is flowing, the hydraulic gradient driving the flow, the area available for flow, and the period of flow. This is described by Darcy's Law (which expresses flow per unit area per unit time):

$$Q/A = K\Delta H \quad (5.2)$$

where

Q/A is volume of water flowing through a unit cross-sectional area per unit time (example units are m3/m2/day)

K is hydraulic conductivity of the porous medium (for example, m/day)

ΔH is hydraulic gradient in the aquifer (for example, m/m).

Parameters

Hydraulic Conductivity

Hydraulic conductivity refers to the property of a soil or other porous material to conduct water. Hydraulic conductivity is characteristic for different materials, and depends on the pore size distribution of the material's matrix.

The hydraulic conductivity of soils is quite variable and is greatest when soils are saturated. Rainfall entering a recharge area wets the soil.

The water content of the soil increases until the soil is saturated. At this stage, water can move directly through the macropores and may bypass part or all of the soil matrix. Macropore characteristics differ with soil types; for instance, macropores in swelling soils operate for only a short time until swelling reduces their size. Water drains readily from the soil until the water content approximates field capacity. At water contents less than field capacity, water movement usually becomes very slow (and is treated as negligible in the following calculations). The long-term (saturated) hydraulic conductivity of soils in significant recharge areas is in the order of 10 to 100 mm/d (0.01 to 0.1 m/d).

The hydraulic conductivity of an aquifer transporting water would be in the order of 0.5 to 10 m/d. In comparison, at a point in the catchment where salting occurs because groundwater flow is restricted, the hydraulic conductivity may be 10 times less (0.05 to 1 m/d).

Hydraulic Gradient

The hydraulic gradient, the driving force acting on the groundwater, is the difference in hydraulic head between two horizontal points (usually points of recharge and discharge) over the horizontal length over which this difference occurs. In an unconfined aquifer, the hydraulic gradient is effectively the gradient of the watertable.

In a permeable soil, the vertical gradient driving recharge is mainly gravity; for every metre of saturated soil depth, there is a hydraulic head of 1 m resulting in a hydraulic gradient of 1 m/m. For water moving horizontally, the driving gradient is the slope of the watertable, so groundwater flow is much slower. The hydraulic gradient of water moving in the groundwater is commonly in the range of 1:100 to 1:1 000 m/m.

The transmission of actual water (or salt) molecules from the point of recharge to the point of discharge takes quite some time. For example, in the Burdekin Irrigation Area (left bank) in north Queensland, the hydraulic gradient is approximately 1:2 300 m/m (11 m difference in hydraulic head between recharge and discharge areas; 25 km from recharge area to discharge area, in this case, the sea). Employing Darcy's Law, a molecule of salt in this catchment would take in the order of 300 years to travel from the recharge area to the sea.

However, salting obviously occurs over much shorter time periods than this. This is because water added to the groundwater system as recharge transmits pressure in the groundwater to the discharge point; it is the equalisation of this pressure that causes the watertable to rise in discharge areas.

Based on these examples of the influence of gradient on water flow, most salting outbreaks will result from the mobilisation of historic salt moving vertically within the soil profile rather than the inflow of salt from naturally saline aquifers.

Area

The surface area of a catchment through which water enters the groundwater as recharge is often much larger than the area through which groundwater can flow out of the catchment. For example, a 1000 ha catchment with developed salting may have restricted subsurface outflow through an aquifer perhaps 100 m wide by 5 m deep. Thus, potential recharge is occurring over a surface area of 10×10^6 m^2 (although not all recharge will be at high rates), whereas outflow is occurring through a cross-sectional area of 500 m^2.

Time Period

In summer rainfall areas, soils are typically saturated for only a few days each year. For saturated hydraulic conductivity to operate, there must be free water at the soil surface to be conducted through the larger pores. This may occur for only two to five days each year. In comparison, a groundwater aquifer is saturated all year round and can conduct water every day of the year.

Interaction of Parameters

In an unsalted catchment at hydrologic equilibrium, recharge will be balanced by subsurface outflow. However, in a salted catchment the rate of recharge will exceed the rate of subsurface outflow. The volume of outflow may be restricted by the cross-sectional area of the aquifer at the point of discharge or by reduced hydraulic conductivity.

Discharge areas develop only after the unsaturated soil water storage is filled and the watertable rises. The period during which the soil water storage becomes saturated provides the lead time that occurs between the initial hydrologic change and the subsequent development of discharge areas. This lead time can range from a few years to up to 50 years. Generalised figures for a salted catchment of 1000 ha (that is, 10×10^6 m^2) with, say, 10% of the catchment having a high recharge rate of 20 mm/d (0.02 m/d), 20% of the catchment having a lower recharge rate of 10 mm/ d (0.01 m/d), and the remaining 70% having a low recharge rate of 3 mm/d (0.003 m/d), averaging over the recharge area to 0.006.m/d. In this illustration, subsurface outflow is likely to occur every day of the year, but recharge will only occur when the soil is saturated down to the watertable.perhaps only two days each year.

The difference between recharge and subsurface outflow (here, between 120 and 18.2 ML/yr) is the volume of water that the system must remove in other ways.

In this situation, the system will compensate and discharge will be increased via:

- increased surface seepage
- increased evaporation from a discharge area with a watertable near the soil surface (At an evaporation rate of 2 mm/d, 73 ML/yr of water will be removed from 10 ha of bare discharge area.)
- increased evapotranspiration from vegetated areas in a low salinity discharge area (due to increased vigour of growth in response to increased water availability).

6

Salinity and Hydrology Management

MANAGING SALINITY BY MANAGING GROUNDWATER BALANCE

A discharge area can be managed by increasing the outflow of groundwater from the catchment until outflow exceeds recharge. However, increasing outflow simply by increasing evaporation and transpiration in the discharge area may not be sustainable in the long term. This is because salt remains and is redistributed to the soil surface or within the root zone. Vegetation in the area will die unless it is able to cope with the more saline conditions. Both the water and salt balances need to be considered because water is the transport mechanism for salt.

Evaporation from surface soil is an energy efficient means of removing free water since the actual evaporation rate often exceeds the actual transpiration rate of vegetation (particularly if the vegetation is affected by waterlogging or salt) and may approximate potential evaporation rates. Researcher determined the critical depth of watertables at which groundwater supply equalled the daily evaporation rate for several soils.

Watertables have to be shallower in heavier clay soils and under conditions of higher daily evaporation rates (for example, in summer) before maximum capillary rise and salting will occur. Surface mulching can reduce the evaporation rate considerably.

Where daily evaporation rates generally exceed 5 mm/d, suggests that watertables need to be within one metre of the soil surface for a considerable part of the year for serious surface soil salting to develop.

MANAGING SOIL SALINITY BY MANAGING LEACHING FRACTION

Accumulated salts can be periodically flushed from the soil profile by seasonal rains or by regular or specific applications of irrigation water. Leaching fraction is the term given to the portion of applied water that is required to drain through the root zone to maintain soil salinity at acceptable concentrations. Researcher used the term leaching requirement and expressed it in terms of the steady state mass balance model discussed earlier:

$$LR = \frac{c_i}{c_o} = \frac{Q_o}{Q_i} \qquad (6.1)$$

where

LR is leaching requirement

Q_i is quantity of water entering the soil (usually expressed as depth)

Q_o is quantity of water draining below the root zone

c_i is concentration of water entering the soil (usually expressed as electrical conductivity)

c_o is concentration of water draining below the root zone (salinity of deep drainage Dd).

This calculation has proved popular for long-term equilibrium situations, although it is strictly only correct where no precipitation of salts or ion exchange occurs within the root zone. Under dryland conditions, Q_i can be readily measured as rainfall and c_i as rainfall salt concentration. Assuming c_o of the drainage water is in equilibrium with the salt concentration of the soil matrix at a water content approaching field capacity, Q_o can be estimated.

Since it is difficult to determine the amount of water draining below the root zone, an estimate of drainage is usually obtained by relating salt concentration at depth to the concentration of the input water (rainfall and irrigation water) weighted for volume of input.

When soils are irrigated with good quality (low salinity/sodicity) water, the amount of rainfall is effectively increased. This increases leaching, and over a period of time a new salt content equilibrium will be established in the soil. Irrigation with good quality water can result in significant removal of salts from the soil profile, as was seen in the Emerald Irrigation Area A new equilibrium is established when the final soil salt concentration is balanced by the amount of water available and the sodicity of the soil.

Many irrigation water quality guidelines promote managing soil leaching by varying the amount of water applied. This works well with permeable soils.

However, in slowly permeable soils (for example, 1 to 10 mm/d), soil properties and sodicity are the dominant controls on leaching rates and reduce the effectiveness of irrigation water management. In clay soils, leaching is strongly influenced by the salt concentration and sodicity of the irrigation water. This problem is obvious with any high-sodium water during and following rainfall because the salt in the surface layers is washed out by rainfall, leading to dispersion and crusting. Very low salinity water almost always results in water infiltration problems, regardless of the proportion of sodium ions in the water. Assessing irrigation water quality with soil properties and behaviour is the best way to avoid these problems.

SOIL STABILITY AND SODICITY

Ion substitution in the clay mineral lattice creates a negative charge on the clay mineral, which attracts cations to the mineral surfaces.

These cations, called exchangeable cations, balance the negative charge of the clay mineral. The properties of the layer of adsorbed cations are determined by the nature of the clay mineral (particularly surface charge density and surface area) and the composition and concentration of the surrounding solution. For example, a high proportion of sodium in the soil solution will result in a high relative proportion of sodium among the exchangeable cations. These characteristics of cations, mineral and surrounding solution determine clay behaviour.

The attractive forces between clay particles are strongest when the exchangeable cations are mostly calcium and weakest when the exchangeable cations are mostly sodium. This is because the cation layer for the divalent calcium cations is smaller, making the distance between the clay particles smaller. This is the main factor contributing to the stability of calciumdominated clays.

The balance between the attractive and repulsive forces between clay particles determines the degree to which a soil will swell or disperse when it is wetted. Swelling is promoted by repulsive forces associated with hydration. If the layer of cations is thick and diffuse (for instance, a cation layer dominated by sodium cations), the greater repulsion between clay particles will result in increased particle separation and dispersion.

Montmorillonite-dominated clays are more stable than clays dominated by other clay minerals. This is because montmorillonite clay minerals attract divalent ions such as calcium (Ca^{2+}) and magnesium (Mg^{2+}) in preference to monovalent ions such as sodium (Na^{+}) and potassium (K^{+}). In contrast, illite minerals display no ionic preference.

Several researchers have identified a non-uniform mixing of divalent and monovalent cations on montmorillonite. For example, researchers considered the affinity of the internal surfaces of montmorillonite for Ca^{2+} to be between two and 15 times greater than the affinity of the external surfaces. Thus in low to moderate Na^{+} concentration solutions, only the outside layers of montmorillonite clay minerals will be affected by sodium, contributing to the greater stability of montmorillonite or cracking clay soils.

Aggregates may slake and/or disperse on wetting. Slaking is the macroscopic breakdown of an unsaturated aggregate on immersion; dispersion is the process of part of an aggregate going into suspension.

The behaviour of clay minerals with sodium has been described by a mechanical model and a physico-chemical model. In the mechanical model, clay behaviour is not very responsive to salt concentration; this is because the clay is based on the interaction of particle shape, particle friction and the geometric arrangement of particles. In the physico-chemical model, salt concentration and ESP cause major changes in clay behaviour.

The mechanical model describes the behaviour of kaolinite clays fairly closely because kaolinite crystals are large and not particularly responsive to salt concentration. On the other hand, the physicochemical model better describes the behaviour of montmorillonite clay minerals because these minerals are responsive to the physico-chemical nature of the medium. Illite clay minerals are intermediate in behaviour.

Mixtures of clay minerals are most sensitive to exchangeable sodium. Researchers found that the order of clay mineral susceptibility to dispersion in sodium bicarbonate solutions was illite (most) > vermiculite > montmorillonite > kaolinite (least).

Researchers represented (in diagrammatic form) the stages and force strengths of slaking, dispersion and flocculation of aggregates under wetting and drying. The mechanisms suggested by Rengasamy and Olsson involve wetting air dry aggregates such that the repulsive forces generated by wetting result in slaking. In a calcium-dominated clay, attractive forces dominate within the microaggregates, resulting in greater stability. As the particles continue to wet, sodium-dominated systems will demonstrate spontaneous dispersion due to the repulsive forces in the exchangeable cation layer. A point is reached where the repulsive and attractive forces are balanced. If the salt concentration of the surrounding solution is raised, flocculation will occur.

The point at which soil just flocculates can be termed the threshold value; this is the balance between repulsive and attractive forces such that the soil remains stable and not dispersed.

If external energy is applied (mechanical dispersion), the clays will disperse when the strength of the repulsive forces exceeds the strength of the attractive forces. Because these processes affect soil structure, they also affect hydraulic conductivity.

The threshold values can be idealised into three regions. Such soils respond to the mechanical effects of bonding and cementing of clays in soils with low clay contents, rather than to physico-chemical effects. Typical of this response would be the behaviour of kaolinitic soils associated with large amounts of iron oxides and the behaviour of acid clay soils with aluminium as the dominant exchangeable cation.

When irrigation waters with a high proportion of sodium ions compared with other cations are added to soil, sodium displaces other cations on the clay mineral exchange sites. This increase in the sodicity of the soil generally results in soil dispersion with consequent soil surface sealing, crusting, erosion, poor water entry and poor seedbeds.

Researchers reported problems with low salinity, low sodicity irrigation waters on silty soils prone to surface dispersion. The effects were attributed to insufficient salts to maintain soil flocculation in the soil surface. This is commonly reported worldwide with low salt content irrigation waters.

7

Features of Salinity Investigations

Soil salinity is the salt content in the soil; the process of increasing the salt content is known as **salinization**. Salt is a natural element of soils and water. Salination can be caused by natural processes such as mineral weathering or the gradual withdrawal of an ocean. It can also be caused by artificial processes such as irrigation.

Salinity is the result of the complex interaction of geologic history, past climate, climate, vegetation, geomorphology (geology and landforms in combination), and land and water development activities on sensitive landscapes. Because of the diverse nature of these interacting factors, there is no one aspect or factor that can identify the risk of salinity or the likely extent of possible salinity problems. Effective management strategies need to be based on salinity risk assessment as well as processes affecting salinity development.

Table 7.1. Features of Salinity Investigations

Feature	Information contributing to salinity investigations	Level I : Initial D : Detailed M : Monitoring
Landscape characteristics and salinity mapping		
Landform feature identification	• Identifies landform features that are hydrologically sensitive and susceptible to salinity • Indicates specific landscape positions where salinity is likely to occur • Indicates areas and landforms most at risk of salinity under changed land use and hydrological conditions • Can provide information about discharge and recharge areas	I : Initial, D
Geology	• Can indicate likely sources of salts • Can reveal geological structures and rock types controlling water movement in the landscape, and provide information on aquifer characteristics	I, D
Landscape salinity mapping	• Provides information about the current extent and severity of salting • Can be used to locate historic salt loads	I (if equipment available), D, M

Vegetation		
Plant communities as salinity indicators	• Indicates location and extent of any current or recurrent saltaffected areas • Can be used to locate areas for more detailed investigations • Useful in uncleared or partly cleared areas or areas under pasture	I
Vegetation patterns on remote sensing	• Variations in density, species composition and images vigour can indicate • Changing vegetation patterns on air photos over time can provide a historical perspective of cyclic variations in salinity and the effects of land use and development	I (field observations), D (remote sensing)
Plant response to salinity and specific ions	• The appearance of individual plants—stunted growth, leaf effects —can indicate plant responses to salinity or high levels of specificions	I, D
Climate and rainfall patterns		
Average annual rainfall characteristics	• Indicates whether land in the region is at risk of watertable salting as characteristics indicated by the correlation between watertable salting occurrences and rainfall patterns	I
Moving average rainfall pattern	• Indicates where the current time fits intolong-term rainfall patterns, pattern and potential for increased or decreased salinity with changes in water inputs (from rainfall or irrigation) over the medium- to long-term	D

Feature	Information contributing to salinity investigations	Level I : Initial D : Detailed M : Monitoring
Soils		
Soil properties	• Indicates areas with a history of waterlogging or salting	I
Soil salinity	• Provides guidelines for the potential of the soil for cropping, pastures, trees	I, D, M
Soil salt profiles	• Indicates current salinity levels and dominant hydrological process • Provides information for choosing species to plant, based on plant salt tolerance data • Can be used to approximately locate recharge and discharge areas and to estimate recharge	I (field 1:5), D (laboratory soils analysis), M
Soil sodicity	• Provides information on soil stability and potential for soil response under irrigation • Provides information for erosion control measures that may be required	D, M
Water		
Field tests for waters	• Indicates salt concentrations, and initial suitability of water for various uses • Mapping water salinity in surface watersand existing groundwater sampling points can indicate salt sources and salinity distribution	I (existing water) (sampl-ing points), D, M

Use of piezometers	• A network of bores or piezometers can be used for regional mapping of groundwater and restrictions to groundwater flow • Monitoring provides insight into processes • Water level contours can indicate barriers to water flow • Suitable for monitoring the effects of management and rainfall variability	I, D, M
Catchment groundwater balance estimation	• Provides an initial assessment of the magnitude of the water imbalance balance • Provides information on the amount of water to be managed to reclaim saline areas	I, D, M
Water chemistry and salt sources identification	• Analysis can be used to indicate likely geologic sources of salts which can sources identification be linked with the actual position of these salt sources in the landscape to interpret hydrologic processes • Indicates mixing of waters and salt concentration processes	
Water quality Human domestic use	• Analyses will indicate suitability for human domestic use	I, D, M
Stock watering	• Analyses will indicate suitability for stock watering	I, D, M
Irrigation	• Analyses will indicate suitability for irrigation depending on soils, climate and crop type • Analyses will indicate potential effects on soil and likelihood of contributing to soil degradation	I, D, M

Feature	Information contributing to salinity investigations	Level I : Initial D : Detailed M : Monitoring
Human activities		
Human land use and records	• Can be useful for identifying specific areas where salinity may have occurred records in the past, and in conjunction with fiveyear moving average rainfall information can indicate areas of the landscape most at risk of salinit under changed hydrologic conditions • Provides a historical perspective on how human activities have contributed to the development of salting • Farm records on land development, bores, water levels etc. can be used to identify past hydrological changes	I (oral history), D (air photos, management recordsetc.)

8

Measurement Techniques and Relationships

ELECTRICAL CONDUCTIVITY AS A MEASURE OF SALINITY

Salinity in soils can be estimated conveniently from the electrical conductivity (EC) of a soil solution. Many salts dissociate to ionic form in water (which, when pure, has a very low conductance), so the electrical conductivity of a solution provides a measure of total concentration of salts.

Three measures of electrical conductivity are:

- $EC_{1:5}$—the electrical conductivity of a 1:5 soil water suspension, used routinely in analyses
- EC_{se}—the electrical conductivity of the soil saturation extract, used for predicting plant response (commonly predicted from 1:5 and soil properties, or can be measured directly)
- EC_{s}—the electrical conductivity of soil at measured or predicted maximum field water content (approximating field capacity), used to assess salt

movement through the soil (usually predicted from 1:5 and soil properties).

$EC_{1:5}$ provides a measure of the content of salts in a 1:5 soil water suspension, the most commonly used method of analysis. EC, chloride (Cl) and pH are usually measured together to provide additional information for interpretation.

The ratio of 1:5 was established in response to difficulties that arise when using the traditional saturation extract mixing method with heavy textured Australian soils. $EC_{1:5}$ is a convenient laboratory and field technique. However, it is not directly related to soil behaviour and plant response because the ratio is far more dilute than is normally found under field conditions and it is fixed irrespective of soil texture. $EC_{1:5}$ results tend to provide an underestimate of the electrical conductivity of sandy soils compared with clay soils.

Plants respond to salinity at water contents equal to or drier than saturation. EC_{se} is the most dilute soil solution concentration that plants could be likely to encounter and has been successfully used to relate plant response to soil salinity for a wide range of soil textures. This saturation water content, a wellaccepted standard, is used because it is the lowest reproducible soil:water ratio for which enough extract can be readily removed for analysis, and it relates in a predictable manner to field soil water contents and soil textures.

A common method for determining saturation water content is mixing the soil with water until the soil paste glistens and begins to flow, and then extracting the solution by filtration under vacuum or pressure, or by centrifuging. An alternative method is to wet the soil sample on a tension table where the soil is placed on a porous material hydraulically linked to free water usually 1 cm below the sample. However, there are problems with these techniques because the wetting end point is not easily reproducible, and with the tension wetting method, the quantity of water taken up by the soil depends on the rate of wetting, the nature of the clay and the amount of exchangeable sodium.

Water (and hence salt) movement in soils becomes very small once the soil water content is drier than maximum field water content (roughly equivalent to the field capacity). ECs represents the salt content at the point where soil profile drainage has essentially ceased, and is determined using centrifuge or other displacement methods. However, technique problems with wetting and extraction result in similar errors to determining EC_{se}. The salinity at maximum field water content is used when estimating leaching fractions and in solute movement studies and modelling as the soil solution is assumed to be in equilibrium with the soil matrix.

Table 8.1 illustrates the relative dilutions above field water content for each of the EC measures.

Table 8.1 Relative dilution above maximum field water content (field capacity) for three measures of soil salinity, $EC_{1:5}$, EC_{se} and EC_s.

Measure	Dilution above maximum field water content (upper drained limit)
EC_s	1 time at depth, equal to field capacity in surface soil
EC_{se}	2 to 3 times at depth, equal to saturated surface soil
$EC_{1:5}$	5 to more than 40 times, depending on soil texture

CONVERTING FROM $EC_{1:5}$ TO EC_{SE}

It is possible to provide mathematical relationships between the EC measures based on water content differences but, because the chemistry of solutions involving dissolution and precipitation and ion exchange are profoundly affected by water content, considerable errors can occur in relating the corresponding EC values.

However, as $EC_{1:5}$ is the most convenient method for determining salinity in soils, techniques for converting to other measures of EC are required.

To relate $EC_{1:5}$ measurements to plant salt tolerance data, soil leaching and soil behaviour, it is necessary to convert $EC_{1:5}$ to EC_{se} (saturation extract).

For pure solutions of salts that are totally soluble in 1:5 soil:water suspensions, the EC of soil at saturation extract would be directly proportional to the EC of the 1:5 suspension.

Expressed as a mass balance equation:

$$Q_{se} EC_{se} = Q_{1:5}\ EC_{1:5} \qquad (8.1)$$

where

Q_{se} is water content equivalent to soil saturation (saturation percentage SP)

EC_{se} is electrical conductivity of salt solution at the water content Q_{se}

$Q_{1:5}$ is water content at equivalent of 1:5 soil: water suspension

$EC_{1:5}$ is electrical conductivity of salt solution at 1:5 soil:water dilution.

To derive EC_{se}, the equation can be rearranged to:

$$EC_{se} = EC_{1.5} \frac{Q_{1.5}}{Q_{se}} \qquad (8.2)$$

$Q_{1:5}$ can be assessed as (500 + 6ADMC) for a 1:5 soil:water suspension (where ADMC is air dry moisture content expressed as kg/100 kg). Thus it is possible to convert from $EC_{1:5}$ to EC_{se} if the ratio of water contents ($Q_{1:5}$: Q_{se}) is known.

However, it is not this simple for a number of reasons:

1. Saturation water content has to be predicted from other soil properties such as air dry moisture content and clay content.
2. Soils contain slowly soluble salts, such as gypsum, sodium carbonate and bicarbonate, and calcium carbonate. These salts are more soluble in dilute solutions, and their solubility depends on the composition of other salts present. For instance, gypsum is more soluble if sodium chloride is present and less soluble if calcium chloride is present. Hence the composition of salts will affect the electrical conductivity of the solution as a whole.
3. $EC_{1:5}$ is usually measured on the solution of soil:water suspensions after mixing and standing. Where some clay remains in suspension, the charge on the clay contributes to $EC_{1:5}$. EC_{se} is measured on extracts without any clay contribution.
4. Increasing dilution results in ion exchange with a preference for monovalent ions such as sodium on the exchange complex. This creates a sink for calcium, resulting in slightly enhanced solubility of calcium salts at greater dilutions compared with non-ion pair forming salts.
5. As a solution becomes more concentrated, dissociated ions pair together forming neutral ion pairs such as $CaSO_4^o$. Since these ion pairs do not conduct electric current, the EC at high concentrations of salts that form ion pairs is reduced. Thus the direct conversion of $EC_{1:5}$ to EC_{se} may overestimate EC_{se} at high salinity levels.

To accurately estimate EC_{se} from $EC_{1:5}$, both the ratio of water contents and the composition of salts need to be known. The water content ratio can be estimated from surrogate soil properties, which include clay content, ADMC, CEC, –33 kPa water content, –1500 kPa water content, and texture (as related to clay content).

The chemistry can be assessed from the concentration of chloride salts in proportion to total salt content. Since the dominant anions in soil water extracts are Cl^- and SO_4^{2-} (with smaller proportions of HCO_3^-, CO_3^{2-} and NO_3^-), and since chloride is often measured routinely with $EC_{1:5}$, the proportional contribution of chloride to the EC can be calculated. The ratio $EC_{1:5}$/ ECCl provides an estimate of the very soluble and sparingly soluble salts present by converting the chloride percentage of the 1:5 soil:water suspension (kg/100 kg soil) to an equivalent EC (dS/m). As ECCl (dS/m) can be closely approximated by 6.64 × $\%Cl_{1:5}$, this calculation can be readily made as:

$$\frac{EC_{1:5}}{EC_{Cl}} = \frac{EC_{1:5}}{Cl\% * 6.64} \quad (8.3)$$

If chloride is expressed as ppm or mg/kg, the bottom line of the above equation becomes:

$$\frac{EC_{1:5}}{EC_{Cl}} = \frac{EC_{1:5}}{(Cl/10000) * 6.64} \quad (8.4)$$

Table 8.2. Relationship between texture class and texture grades and approximate clay contents

Texture class	Texture grades	Median clay content (approx.) %
sand	sand	5
loamy sand	loamy sand, clayey sand	7
sandy loam	sandy loam	15
silty loam	loam, silty loam	25
clay loam	clay loam, silty clay loam	32
light clay	light clay, light medium clay	40
medium clay	medium clay	50
heavy clay	heavy clay	65

The concentration of very soluble salts will change linearly with changes in water content (as modelled in the mass balance equation at the start of this section). However, the concentration of sparingly soluble salts that form saturated solutions at the water contents under discussion will not change linearly with changes in water content. In these cases, EC_{se} cannot be accurately estimated from $EC_{1:5}$ if a linear relationship is assumed. The proportion of the EC contributed by soluble salts must be known for reasonably accurate conversions.

LEACHING FRACTION

An estimate of leaching fraction is important when considering the suitability of a soil for irrigation or for determining the likely impact of land use change on the amount of water moving below the root zone to the groundwater system. Measurement of leaching under field conditions presents large logistical problems and the use of deterministic solute models to predict leaching requires water application estimates, plant water use estimates and detailed description of soil hydraulic properties. Therefore, a simple empirical approach was developed by the researchers to predict salt leaching for dryland soils and which is also applicable to irrigation.

ROOT ZONE SALINITY

Plants respond to salinity throughout the root zone, so it is useful to be able to convert measurements at various depths in the root zone into a single number that can be used when considering plant response. Two measures of root zone salinity are commonly used: average, and water uptake weighted. Both require an estimate of root depth for the particular plant species under consideration.

Average Root Zone Salinity

Because plants respond to the integration of atmospheric and soil conditions, averaging the salinity for the root zone depth (average root zone salinity) will provide a conservative measure of soil salinity conditions for estimating plant response.

Several studies have shown average root zone salinity to provide an appropriate estimate of root zone salinity for determining plant response to salinity.

Average root zone salinity is calculated from soil profile salinity data by summing the salinity measurements for a series of root zone depth increments and dividing by the number of increments. Water uptake weighted root zone salinity Many Australian soils have reduced soil porosity, hydraulic conductivity and water storage capacity with depth, and increasing salinity with increasing depth.

Thus a measure of root zone salinity weighted for the actual water uptake pattern of plants in the root zone would possibly provide a more realistic estimate of plant response than a measure that averages root zone conditions.

The weighted measure is based on the concepts that water is more available to plants in the less saline areas of the root zone and that water uptake by roots is not uniform throughout the root zone. In fact, the shape of the water uptake pattern with depth varies considerably with frequency of rainfall and/or irrigation.

Some general and specific approaches to water uptake with depth have been used based on root length density and more generic rooting patterns. The approach is appropriate where subsoil salinities are high because roots cannot remove much water in these situations.

Researcher found that 40% of soil water extraction by plants occurred within the top quarter of the root zone depth, 30% in the second quarter depth, 20% in the third quarter depth and 10% in the fourth quarter. This relationship has been widely used, and is quite similar to that determined for cracking clay soils at Emerald under 10 to 14 day irrigation. Under conditions of frequent irrigation, higher proportions of soil water extraction are likely in the top 25% of the root zone.

Researchers considered another exponential water uptake pattern. Their pattern probably places too much emphasis on the surface soil depths and underestimates the amount of water available to plants at lower depths in the root zone.

In this chapter, a 40:30:20:10 proportional water uptake pattern for each quarter of the root zone has been adopted for both dryland conditions and irrigated conditions where some water stress will occur. Water uptake weighted root zone salinity probably provides a better representation of root zone salinity where subsoils are saline. This is typical of many less permeable soils in Australia since subsoil salinity indicates reduced wetting and thus limited water availability.

SODICITY IN SOILS AND WATERS

The two most common measures of sodicity are:

- exchangeable sodium percentage (ESP), which is the proportion of sodium adsorbed onto the clay mineral surfaces as a proportion of the total cation exchange capacity
- sodium adsorption ratio (SAR), which is the relative concentration of sodium to calcium and magnesium in the soil solution or (irrigation) water.

ESP is a measure of soil sodicity and SAR is a measure of soil solution or water sodicity. The relationship between the SAR of the soil solution at saturation and the ESP is given in USSL and is generally applicable to a wide range of soils.

Soils with high montmorillonite clay content (those that swell and shrink) can tolerate higher ESP than clay soils with limited capacity to swell and shrink. This is because the restructuring of the soil during swelling and shrinking overcomes some of the problems caused by dispersed clay. However, wet dispersed soils (regardless of clay content) will have reduced infiltration and be prone to increased runoff and erosion.

Magnesium associated with sodium has commonly been thought to aid soil dispersibility. There is considerable evidence that this effect is much more applicable to illite soils than montmorillonite soils, although further research is required. Some researchers propose that low exchangeable Ca:Mg ratios in conjunction with ESP indicate enhanced dispersion. There is still debate about the role of Mg. The alternative view is that Ca causes flocculation, Na causes dispersion, and Mg acts in a fairly neutral manner and, in the absence of Ca, can increase the effects of Na to some extent.

High salt concentration will flocculate the clay and maintain aggregation and hydraulic conductivity. The actual thresholds at which this occurs vary with clay type and ESP.

ESP

ESP is determined by routine CEC and exchangeable cation methodologies as outlined by the researchers. Soluble cations are removed via a washing step and the exchangeable cations (which are subsequently analysed) are displaced by ammonium ions (at a nominated pH). The total CEC is determined by displacing and analysing the ammonium ions.

ESP is calculated as follows:

$$ESP = \frac{100Na^+}{CEC} \tag{8.5}$$

In the absence of CEC data, the sum of the concentrations of the cations Na^+, Ca^{2+}, Mg^{2+} and K^+ can be used as an approximation of CEC except:

- in acid soils where the summation of cation concentrations will provide an overestimate of ESP
- in alkaline soils where Tucker's solution at pH 8.4 has not been used to extract cations, since sparingly soluble calcium salts will inflate the value for Ca^{2+} concentration value and hence provide an underestimate of ESP.

In some variable charge soils (usually acid soils), the summation of the concentrations of the four cations may provide an overestimate of CEC, due to pH-dependent charge, and ESP calculated using this CEC may be an underestimate. A more appropriate measure of CEC is necessary for these soils.

SAR

Sodium adsorption ratio (SAR) is calculated as follows:

$$\mathrm{SAR} = \frac{\mathrm{Na}^{+}}{\left(0.5(\mathrm{Ca}^{2+} + \mathrm{Mg}^{2+})\right)^{0.5}} \tag{8.6}$$

where ionic concentrations are in meq/L, determined from the soluble ions in the saturation extract. (If units of mmolec/L are used, the calculation is the same as equation 20 above. However, if units of mmole/L are used, the concentration of calcium and magnesium ions should not be halved.

9

Landscape Characteristics and Salinity Mapping

LANDFORM FEATURE IDENTIFICATION

Geological features and past patterns of weathering make some landforms more hydrologically sensitive and susceptible to salting than others. The important feature of sensitive landforms is the presence of some restriction to groundwater flow that causes the watertable to rise to near the soil surface, resulting in a discharge area with evaporative concentration of salts. Watertable salting commonly occurs in positions in the landform indicated as potential discharge areas in the diagrams accompanying the following descriptions (Figure 9.1).

Hydrologically sensitive landscapes often show evidence of past seepages or shallow watertables. If development in these types of landscapes changes the hydrological balance, salting may occur as a result.

Landforms occur in patterns in regions and can be compared readily within a region. Once identified, they are useful for indicating sensitive areas of the landscape which can be further investigated. Landform features will also determine which management strategies may be effective.

The advantage of using landforms to diagnose susceptibility is that landforms can be readily observed without undertaking detailed (and sometimes expensive) site investigations.

SOURCES OF INFORMATION

- Inspecting the property and other properties in the catchment is the most direct way of identifying landform features.
- In some cases, it may be easier to identify landforms on aerial photographs or topographical and geological maps.
- Landforms in some areas may have already been identified and discussed in land or soil survey reports.

LANDFORM FEATURE DESCRIPTIONS

Basalt Form

The most common landform associated with salinity in Queensland, this landform comprises both recent and highly weathered basalt flows overlying less permeable sandstones and mudstones at fairly shallow depths (Fig. 9.1). Basalt

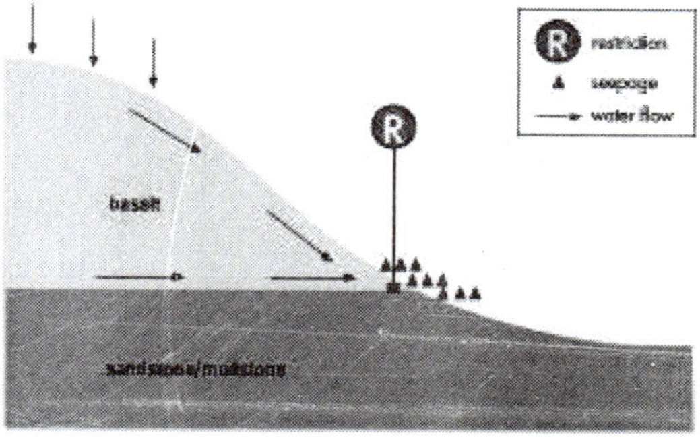

Figure 9.1. Basalt form

which is fractured, columnar or vesicular forms suitable groundwater recharge areas and transmission zones. Basalt gravels in old valley infill areas also form aquifers which readily transport water.

The restriction to downward water movement is provided by the underlying material which, being less permeable than the overlying basalt, restricts continued downward water movement. In addition, layering within the basalt and bole (previously weathered) layers provides regions of variable permeabilities which can contribute to salting.

Seepages or shallow watertables occur at the interface areas. The basalt form is characterised by both seepage and watertable salting with source waters (usually of low salinities) concentrated by evaporation. This form is evident on the eastern Darling Downs, central Queensland and on lateritised basalts in the Rockhampton and Kingaroy areas.

Catena Form

This form occurs where soil forming processes and wetness have resulted in a change in soil properties down a slope. The form comprises shallow soils in upslope positions overlying weathered parent material with soils gradually becoming deeper and heavier textured downslope extending onto flat heavy clay alluvial areas (Fig. 9.2).

Figure 9.2. Catena form

Sodicity may be high at the base of the slope, further restricting permeability. More recent infills of clays at the bottom of the slope can restrict outflow. Soils at break-of-slope positions tend to be saline at some depth, indicating a past history of high watertables. Restricted drainage results in salt accumulation.

The change in hydraulic gradient creates a similar effect to a barrier to water movement. Salting results from infiltration of water into the soils and lateral movement through the weathered parent material or through more permeable soil horizons. Discharge occurs in the lower slope or break-of-slope positions where the heavier clays or geologic features (for instance, dykes) restrict water movement. In some situations, the weathered parent material can act as a confined aquifer contained by the less permeable soils above and the less weathered rock below.

Alluvial Fan

This form occurs where the coarser sediments of an old alluvial fan have been subsequently buried or partially buried by clays (Figure 28c). Subsurface water flowing from upslope areas or old stream channels enters the alluvia of the former land surface which acts as an aquifer for water transmission. Discharge areas occur where heavy clays, more recent alluvia, or finer sediments are deposited over the coarser materials at the margins of the alluvial fans.

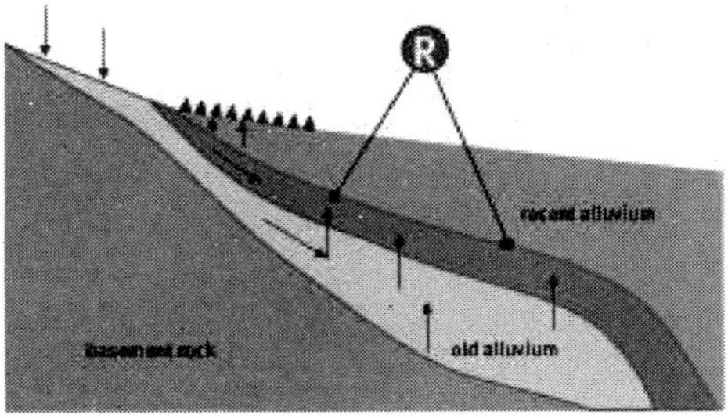

Figure 9.3. Alluvial fan

Catchment Restriction—Roadway

This type of restriction occurs on heavy clay areas where roads and stock routes across alluvia have compacted the soils, particularly in wet periods. This reduces the water transmission properties of the soils sufficiently to raise watertables and cause salting upslope of the road.

Catchment Restriction—Natural

Rock bars or resistant sediments can restrict water flow in valley floors or where existing aquifers thin out. The catchment throat is often narrowed in width and/or depth. Discharge areas develop in the region upslope of the restriction.

Alluvial Valley

This is a particular form of catchment restriction where a geologic restriction to water flow out of a catchment results in the deposition of alluvium (Fig. 9.4). These valleys are usually associated with a very low hydraulic gradient.

Water quality modelling in the Lockyer, Callide and Dee valleys indicates that in these systems the major process of salt accumulation is the extraction of water from capillary fringes of aquifers by deep-rooted vegetation. Accumulated salts are leached back into the aquifer system, increasing salinity. Additional geomorphic and geological restrictions to water flow can intensify these effects by

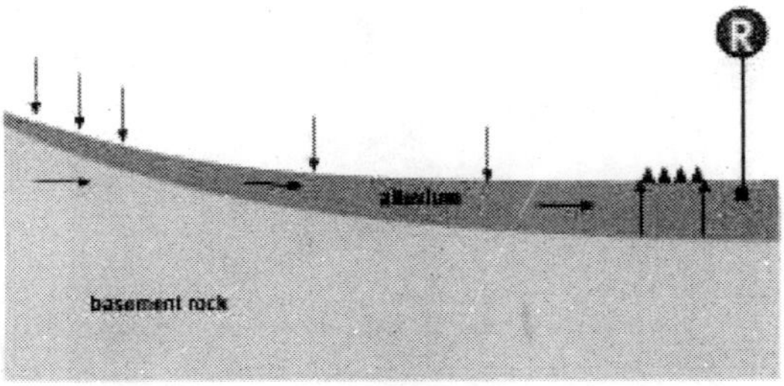

Figure 9.4. Alluvial valley

raising groundwater levels. In these valleys, salinity gradients increase with distance from the head of the valley.

Where heavy clay alluvium has been deposited on top of permeable materials, salting may extend over large areas due to the upward movement of water under hydraulic pressure. This particularly occurs in granitic landscapes where the high proportion of sodium released on weathering results in sodic clays of low permeability in valley floors. Upward flow through this confining layer contributes to salting by evaporative concentration.

Confluence of Streams

At the junction of a minor stream with a major stream, the reduction in flow velocity and resultant deposition of suspended particles at the junction results in a greater proportion of clay in the sediments at this point with lower lateral permeability. This occurs particularly in the smaller stream immediately upstream of the junction.

Dykes

Geologic dykes can form areas of variable permeability in the landscape. Where less fractured or weathered dykes occur across the direction of slope, water movement downslope is interrupted and incipient or permanent salting areas develop (Fig. 9.5).

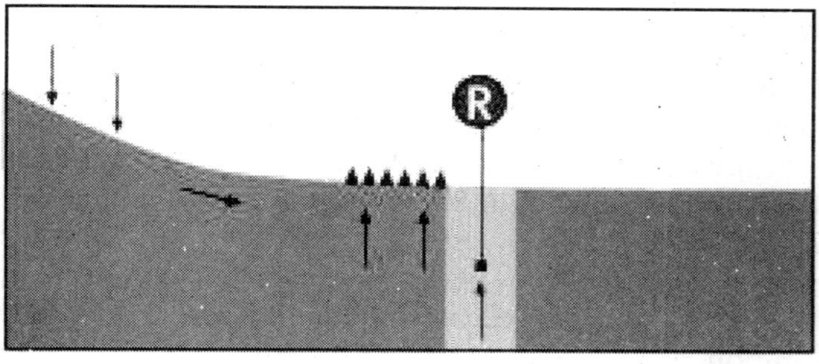

Figure 9.5: Dyke

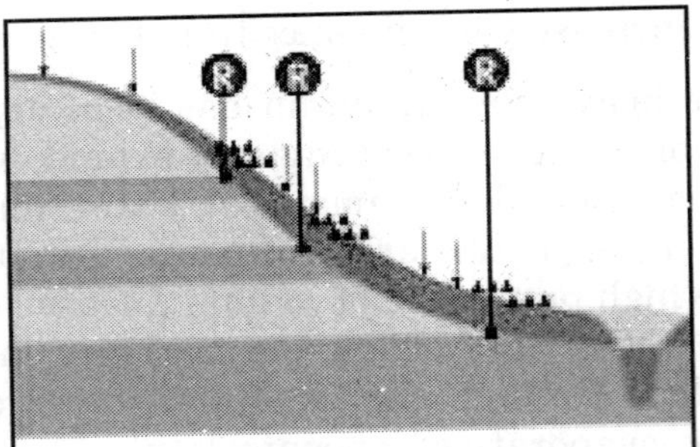

Figure 9.6: Stratigraphic form

Stratigraphic Form

Variable permeabilities in sedimentary rock layers can act as preferential flow paths or imperme-able areas under increased water regimes. In this situation, small seepages and salted areas appear on hillslopes in response to variations in the permeability of different rock layers (Fig. 9.6).

Geological Faulting

Faulting can operate in a similar manner to dykes or alternatively can provide preferential upward flow paths for water. The mound springs around the southern fringes of Lake Eyre and the seepage in the Yelarbon desert region are classic cases of the latter form of geological faulting.

Dams

A dam can contribute to salting both upstream and downstream of the dam itself. The dam also acts as a hydraulic barrier to groundwater flow. Upstream salting results from reduced hydraulic gradient of downslope flow caused by the raised water level of the dam. Downstream salting results from leakage of water, usually above a shallow, less permeable subsoil layer. This form is relatively common.

Lakes (groundwater terminus)

Regions where surface water and groundwater terminate with limited outflow and hence flushing are generally salted due to evaporative concentration (Fig.9.7).

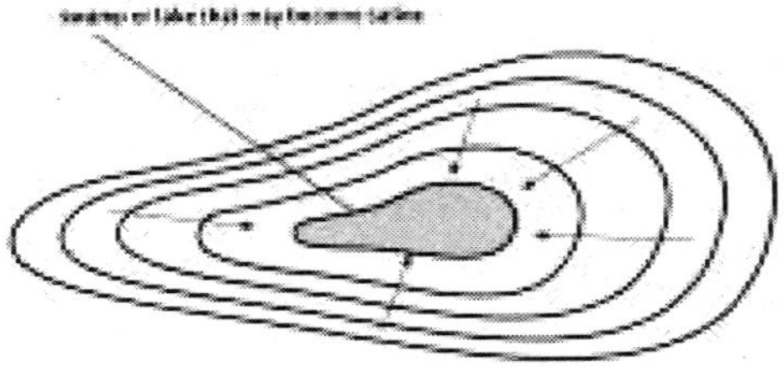

Figure 9.7: Lakes (groundwater terminus)

GEOLOGY

Most dissolved salts occurring in natural waters originate from the combination of salts in rainfall and weathering of rocks near the land surface. High salinities occur in many of the fine-grained sedimentary rocks (mudstone and shales). Also, and more importantly, geological structures can control water movement in landscapes. By identifying underlying geological formations, information is obtained which will facilitate the identification of landform features in the region.

Landscape Salinity Mapping

The mass and extent of salt in the landscape can be estimated and mapped using a number of remote sensing and contact and non-contact ground-based geophysical methods. Using these methods, areas of potential salinity hazard and salt loads likely to be mobilised under a wetter equilibrium can be identified.

Electromagnetic induction instruments facilitate a rapid assessment of amount and extent of soil salinity. These instruments induce a magnetic field in the soil from a primary electric current in a coil held above the soil surface. The strength of the magnetic field is proportional to the electrical conductance of the soil as measured by secondary current induced in a receiver coil. The spacing of the emitter and receiver coils determines the depth of the reading. The depth response function is significantly more responsive at the soil surface. The advantages of using electromagnetic induction instruments are being able to obtain continuous readings and the lack of soil contact.

Three instruments are commonly used:

- EM.38, with sensing depth to approximately 1.5 m, suitable for relating surface soil salinity to plant growth
- EM.31, with sensing depth to approximately 6 m, more suitable for landscape salt and salting processes as well as providing a useful indication of surface soil salinity
- EM.34.3, with three coil spacings giving a maximum sensing depth of up to 60 m, useful for investigating landscape salt loads at deeper depths.

LANDSCAPE SALINITY HAZARD CLASSIFICATION

There are a number of schemes for classifying land according to its salinity status. The guidelines developed by the Dryland Salinity working group are used here. This classification scheme (Table 9.1) evaluates land on the basis of the current degree of salting as well as the degree of salinity risk under changed land use or land management conditions (based on watertable salting).

While it is difficult to estimate severity by any universally applicable objective criteria, these classes offer a framework to describe what is happening or what may be expected to happen in an area. By using standard terms such as these, salt-affected areas can be mapped and described in different regions using comparable criteria.

Table 9.1 Classes of salt-affected land

Class	Description
Not at risk	Land not predisposed to watertable salting regardless of land use or management
Stable	Land predisposed to watertable salting but unlikely to become saline under existing land use or management
At risk	Land predisposed to watertable salting which is likely to become saline under existing land use or management
Slightly affected	Land showing a reduction in non salttolerant plant vigour, some salt-tolerant plants, seasonally or permanently shallow watertable, and perhaps small bare areas
Moderately affected	Land showing a significant loss of non salt-tolerant plants, salt-tolerant plants are common, seasonally or permanently shallow watertable, bare areas up to about 5 m^2 in size, some erosion present
Severel affected	Land showing an absence of non salttolerant plants, permanently shallow watertable, large bare areas which are often badly eroded

10

Vegetation

PLANT COMMUNITIES AS SALINITY INDICATORS

Certain species are commonly found on salt-affected soils and can be useful for identifying salt outbreaks. Where plant species are identified that are salttolerant or that compete more effectively under saline conditions, salinity may be occurring at the site. Where species that are not salt-tolerant are present in surrounding areas but are absent from a location, this may also indicate soil salting.

TREES AND SHRUBS

Tea tree (*Melaleuca* sp.) is commonly associated with many watertable salting occurrences; black tea tree (*Melaleuca bracteata*) particularly so. Historical data and current presence of tea tree indicate water levels were shallow prior to clearing in most areas now affected by watertable salting.

Some small areas may have perched watertables that are local and unconnected with regional groundwaters. Perched watertables often support a tea tree understorey beneath eucalypt forest, whereas permanently shallow regional groundwater levels usually support pure tea tree stands. Also, shallow regional groundwater levels occur in lowest landscape positions, whereas localised perched watertables can occur in higher landscape locations.

Where the presence of black tea tree, tea tree generally (*Melaleuca* sp.) and other local native vegetation species indicate the watertable is less than 6 m beneath the soil surface under native vegetation, there is a high risk of water rising to the surface if the vegetation is cleared.

There is little published information relating trees and watertable depths. In areas in where the watertable was 6 m below the soil surface under native vegetation, salting occurred after the vegetation was cleared. The watertable salting occurred in areas cleared of stands of black tea tree where the watertable was at a depth of 5 m to 6 m prior to clearing. Plants and plant communities which often indicate recharge and discharge areas are listed in Table 10.1.

Table 10.1. Plant species and communities that can indicate features of interest in salinity investigations

Species or community	Indicates
Black tea tree (*Melaleuca bracteata*)	shallow groundwater—potential discharge area
Tea tree generally	
Melaleuca bracteata	saline soil
Melaleuca nodosa	
Brigalow (*Acacia harpophylla*)	
Melaleuca spp. generally	poor drainage—potential
Luxuriant grass and tree growth	discharge area or stream boundary
Softwood scrub	recharge areas
Angophora sp.	
Cypress pine	
Silver-leaved ironbark	
Narrow-leaved ironbark	

Pasture

The combination and relative abundance of species provides the best indication of salt levels, rather than the occurrence of any particular species. In general, poor pasture condition, including patchy growth, reduced vigour and loss of saltsensitive plants, can indicate salinity.

A number of factors interact to determine species composition in a particular pasture. These factors include grazing regime, past management history (cultivation etc.), seed sources, soil conditions (such as compaction or low fertility) and seasonal influences. For instance, creeping saltbush (*Atriplex semibaccata*) can be a good indicator of salinity as it occurs on saline or disturbed soils. However, this species is also generally absent from intensively grazed paddocks.

The composition of species in salt-affected areas is not dramatically distinct from those found on non-saline soils. Gradual changes in vegetation occur across the transition from non-saline through marginal to saline soil. Rhodes grass, green couch and wild aster generally persist in all but the most severely salt-affected patches.

Marine couch (*Sporobolus virginicus*), green couch, brown beetle grass, samphire, creeping saltbush, pigweed (*Portulaca oleracea*), coastal pigface (*Sesuvium portulacastrum*) and soft roly-poly (*Salsola kali*) occur on severely saline soils, while on the less saline margins purpletop Rhodes grass (*Chloris inflata*), woodland lovegrass (*Eragrostis sororia*) and boobialla (*Myoporum acuminatum*) are found. Beyond this zone on relatively non-saline soils, black spear grass (*Heteropogon contortus*) communities commonly occur.

VEGETATION PATTERNS ON REMOTE SENSING IMAGES

Vegetation density and growth vigour usually reflect the available water regime. Potential recharge and discharge areas can often be deduced from remote sensing images, preferably obtained before natural vegetation was initially cleared. Ground truthing must always be used to verify aerial photo interpretation. In this case, the increased vegetation density identified on the photograph was not due to increased wetness and thus was not a potential discharge area.

PLANT RESPONSE TO SALINITY AND SPECIFIC IONS

Most agriculturally important crops respond to total salinity as an osmotic effect. Some woody horticultural species are also susceptible to concentrations of specific ions. When these concentrations reach toxic levels, effects are most noticeable in the leaves, particularly in the leaf margins. Symptoms include necrotic spots, leaf bronzing and, in highly toxic cases, defoliation. The ions most often involved are sodium, chloride and boron.

For a given species, an assessment of plant salt tolerance will depend on the purpose of growing the plant. Plant salt tolerance for crops is defined as the ability of plants to survive and produce economic yields under saline conditions. For ornamental species, the ability to survive and maintain an aesthetic appearance may be more important than yield.

Plant Stage of Growth

While some species are more susceptible to salinity at emergence than at later stages of growth, other species are in fact less susceptible at emergence. In these species, a crop that appears to have germinated successfully under saline conditions may fail at a later stage of growth. Hence, the effects of salt both on germination and yield should be considered when choosing crops for marginal conditions.

Management Practices

Some species can tolerate higher salinity concentration in the soil than in water applied to the leaves. This is specifically relevant to crops under sprinkler irrigation. Management practices for using marginally saline waters include irrigating below the leaves (to avoid depositing salts on the leaves) and irrigating at night (to reduce salt on the leaves left by rapid evaporation during the day).

SYMPTOMS OF SALINITY AND SPECIFIC ION EFFECTS ON PLANTS

The most common indications of salinity occur when plants are stunted, grow slowly, or do not grow at all. In some cases, leaves may be a darker green and more succulent than usual. However, in most cases, the only indication will be reduced yield; dry matter production may be affected less than yield. Salttolerant species such as pioneer Rhodes grass and green couch are often more productive in areas where watertables are close to the surface due to increased moisture availability.

Some plants which are osmotically stressed by salt show no distinctive symptoms apart from the ones mentioned in the previous section and others related to normal water stress. Salt stress for most plants is an additional stress to water stress because the plant cannot develop sufficient energy to extract water.

Woody species tend to show more leaf damage than herbaceous species. In woody species, leaf burn and even defoliation can indicate salinity. These symptoms tend to result more from the accumulation of specific ions (such as sodium or chloride) than from total salt concentration.

In addition, other elements not related to salinity, such as heavy metals, can cause a number of symptoms that are similar to salinity and specific ion effects.

Sodium

Excess sodium accumulates in the leaves, causing leaf burn, necrotic patches and even defoliation. (This is an effect of plants' response to high levels of a specific ion rather than to salinity in general.) Poor physical conditions in the soil (caused by sodicity) will limit plant growth (the major effect). Plants may experience calcium and magnesium deficiencies because of reduced availability.

Excess sodium will degrade the physical properties of a soil. Sodic soils tend to disperse readily, affecting air and water permeability, and form hard, dense clods when the soil dries. These physical effects prevent adequate root development and increase the difficulties of soil management. Limited root exploitation can result in nutritional deficiencies and greater likelihood of water stress. Sodicity problems occur less often on sandy soils and are compensated to some extent by swelling and shrinkage on cracking clay soils.

Under continued irrigation with strongly sodic waters, the exchangeable cations on the clay mineral surfaces of the soil are gradually replaced by sodium until a new equilibrium is established. Deficiencies of calcium tend to arise because it precipitates out of solution as $CaCO_3$ as the sodium exchanges onto the clay in alkaline soils. This occurs to a greater extent if the irrigation waters contain high levels of bicarbonate. Waters containing sodium bicarbonate (residual alkali) can develop soil pH up to 10.0, creating significant nutritional problems.

Chloride

Plants affected by chloride toxicity exhibit similar foliar symptoms to sodium, such as leaf bronzing and necrotic spots in some species. Defoliation occurs in some woody species.

Chloride behaves similarly to sodium. However, salinity impacts on citrus yield, long attributed to chloride levels in waters, have recently been found to be more closely related to EC. The evidence for specific yield reduction in citrus in relation to chloride or osmotic effects is a matter of debate. The current evidence strongly indicates that osmotic effects are the primary cause of yield reduction.

Boron

Symptoms, such as yellowing margins, crumpling, blackening and distortion, appear first in the youngest leaves. The level at which a particular plant will find boron toxic depends on a variety of factors, particularly whether the boron originates in the soil or in the irrigation water.

11

Soils

SOIL PROPERTIES

A soil's properties and behaviour largely determine how much water will move through the soil as deep drainage. Soil profile morphology can be a useful indicator of past salting or wetness. Salting outbreaks commonly occur on clay soils. Duplex soils may be associated with salting adjacent to the salted area.

Soil characteristics such as mottling, colour and manganese and iron distribution in the profile indicate soil wetness. Researcher undertook a detailed study of the relationship between soil morphology and high watertables in the Ingham area. From the characteristics of soil mottles (amount, size, contrast and colour) and soil colour, the number of days a watertable fluctuates in a horizon and the number of days of waterlogging could be predicted.

Soil morphology is particularly useful for identifying catena landforms where soils are the product of weathering and salinisation under past water regimes. Examples are solodic and solonised solonetz soils in lower slope positions.

Soil pH

Acid soils (pH < 6.5) tend to be soils with moderate to high deep drainage rates. Generally, the mmore acid the soil, the greater the deep drainage rate.

Neutral pH soils (6.5–7.5) are generally reasonably permeable. Alkaline soils (pH 7.6–8.7) characteristically contain $CaCO_3$ in the profile. The equilibrium pH for $CaCO_3$ is approximately 8.4 (depending on the partial pressure of CO_2). Soils in this pH range have relatively low recharge rates unless derived from basaltic parent materials or other geological formations high in calcium.

Strongly alkaline soils (pH > 8.7) indicate the presence of sodium carbonate or sodium bicarbonate since these two carbonates dissociate into a strong alkali. High pH is often characteristic of highly sodic soils since any available calcium is usually precipitated as $CaCO_3$. The remaining sodium replaces ions on the clay exchange sites.

Concretions

Massive or numerous nodules of calcium carbonate ($CaCO_3$) at varying depths in the soil profile (but generally within the top 0.6 to 0.9 m) can indicate a historic seepage of waters with high calcium content. $CaCO_3$ precipitates out of solution on concentration or when the partial pressure of CO_2 is reduced, such as at a watertable surface (see Processes controlling ionic composition page 74). $CaCO_3$ nodules tend to occur in areas with high levels of calcium in the groundwater, such as in basalt regions.

At the water–air interface in groundwaters rich in iron or manganese, oxidation results in the precipitation of iron oxides and/or manganese oxides as nodules or concretions, referred to as iron and manganese nodules. This occurs in acid soils.

Clay Content and Mineralogy

Cracking clay soils have variable rates of deep drainage depending on the subsoil sodicity. More sodic soils have lower deep drainage rates. Low ESP soils have higher deep drainage rates, even with very high clay content, because the soils develop good structure. Soil depth is also a factor: deeper cracking clay soils have high plant-available water capacity and low redistribution of infiltrated water, resulting in lower deep drainage than shallower soils.

Because high clay content montmorillonite soils are often low in sodium, they form well-structured, relatively permeable soils. Black earth soils with as much as 70% clay content can be quite permeable. Soils with kaolinite mineralogy are usually more permeable than soils with mixed clay mineralogy, such as kaolinite combined with montmorillonite or with illite.

SOIL SALINITY

A range of direct and indirect laboratory and field methods are used to measure soil salinity. The first two tests in the table, EC of a 1:5 soil:water suspension and saturation extract, are described in detail in Electrical conductivity as a measure of salinity.

Techniques for measuring $EC_{1:5}$

Field Method

This method is appropriate for quick field tests. Field test results will differ from laboratory results because soil drying, shaking and settling times are not standardised in the field. However, to simply identify the order of magnitude of a salinity problem, these factors can be ignored.

1. Add approximately 10 mL of distilled water, rainwater or tank water (or other water, if none of these is available) to a centrifuge tube.

2. Add small soil aggregates (to reduce breakdown time) until the contents of the tube increase by 5 mL to bring the volume to 15 mL.
3. Add additional water to bring the total volume to 30 mL.
4. Shake intermittently for 5 minutes and allow to settle for 5 minutes.
5. Dip an EC probe into the supernatant solution (rather than the sediment) and take a reading.

Note: A field test such as this provides a useful approximation of $EC_{1:5}$, and correcting for bulk density will not improve the accuracy of the reading. Since field soils are often moist to wet, any bulk density effects will be confounded by moisture content. In surface soils, bulk density is about 1 000 to 1 500 kg/m^3, and in subsoils, up to 2000 kg/m^3. There are as many errors in reading the water level on the centrifuge tube as in correcting for bulk density.

Laboratory Method

Soils are air dried (at 40°C) and ground (to less than 2 mm particles) and then mixed into suspension in a solution of one part soil to five parts deionised water at 25°C. After shaking for one hour and settling for one hour, the EC, pH and Cl are measured.

SOIL SALT PROFILES

An examination of salt profile shapes to a depth of, say, 1.5 m to 2 m is a fast and simple method of determining the hydrologic processes that may be occurring in a specific location in a catchment.

SOIL SODICITY

The two most common measures of soil sodicity are:

- exchangeable sodium percentage (ESP), being the proportion of sodium adsorbed onto the clay mineral surfaces as a proportion of total cation exchange capacity
- sodium adsorption ratio (SAR), being the relative concentration of sodium to calcium and magnesium in the soil solution.

Measures of sodicity are explained in detail in Sodicity in soils and waters Soils of 30% to 50% clay with mixed mineralogy are most sensitive to ESP. In surface soils unprotected by crop cover or mulch (and therefore subject to rainfall energy), an ESP value of 3 is possibly a more accurate measure of 'non-sodic'. For silty soils in Israel, for example, a surface ESP of only 1 to 1.5 will contribute to soil crusting and reduced infiltration.

The labels are the infiltration rate (mm/hr) for the irrigation water EC and soil ESP of the 0-76 mm depth of the soil columns. These data illustrate that there is no predefined threshold value of ESP above which soil permeability dramatically decreases. The equilibrium lines are similar to the hydraulic conductivity values, indicating the interdependence and effect of EC and ESP in maintaining the hydraulic conductivity of soils.

12

Waters

FIELD TESTS FOR WATERS

Field tests are useful as a preliminary survey of the extent and distribution of salinity in a catchment or area. Water samples can be obtained from existing water access points (streams, wells, bores, irrigation channels, dams), but the accuracy of the survey will be limited by the spatial distribution of these points. Ideally, sampling points should be selected to represent a range of local geomorphological features (including soils and aquifers) and land uses.

SALINITY AND CHEMICAL COMPOSITION

Salinity in water samples can be determined on-site using an EC meter, or samples can be forwarded to a laboratory for testing of salinity and chemical composition. Samples for laboratory analysis should be forwarded as quickly as possible. Delays and high temperatures will result in salts precipitating out of solution, changing the chemical composition of the water. A wide range of EC meters is available, ranging from small pocket meters costing around $80, to small field meters with temperature compensation costing about $250, to multi-function extended range EC meters costing upwards of $300. Mid-range meters with builtin temperature compensation are appropriate for most salinity investigations.

The accuracy of the cheaper models is limited and these models are not calibrated readily. Cheaper meters are often unable to read salinity levels less than 0.1 dS/m or greater than 20 dS/m. If dealing with an EC greater than 20 dS/m using a cheaper EC meter, a measure can be obtained by diluting the sample, measuring the diluted sample, and multiplying the result by the dilution factor.

Temperature has a significant effect on EC. If the EC meter in use does not have a temperature compensated probe, readings should be adjusted to the standard temperature of 25oC using the following formula:

$$\ln K_{t2} = \ln K_{t1} + \beta_1(t_2 - t_1) - \beta_2(t_2^2 - t_1^2) \qquad (12.1)$$

where

K_{t1} is conductivity (EC reading) at field temperature of sample

K_{t2} is conductivity (corrected EC reading) at standard temperature of 25°C

t_1 is field temperature of sample being tested for conductivity

t_2 is 25 (standard temperature)

β_1 is 0.029 (coefficient for local natural waters)

β_2 is 0.00019 (coefficient for local natural waters).

DEPTH TO THE WATERTABLE

The depth to the watertable can be measured using a plopper or other indicating device attached to a tape measure that can be lowered down a bore. A plopper is simply a device that makes a plopping sound when it strikes the water surface. Old valves from internal combustion engines (preferably with concave faces) and brass plugs with concave faces make serviceable ploppers.

A plopper can also be constructed from a 20-25 mm pipe with a cork or stopper blocking the inside of the pipe about 5 mm from the bottom end. Whistles and electrical devices can also be used.

It is important to record the reference point usedfor measurement; this is usually either ground level or the top of the bore. For salinity investigations, it is preferable to measure from the watertable to ground level.

The following steps should ensure an accurate measure:

- Measure the distance from the bottom of the plopper to the end of the tape where it is attached to the plopper. Add on this amount each time a measurement is taken.
- Lower the plopper into the bore until the plopper enters the groundwater. Pull up the tape slowly,

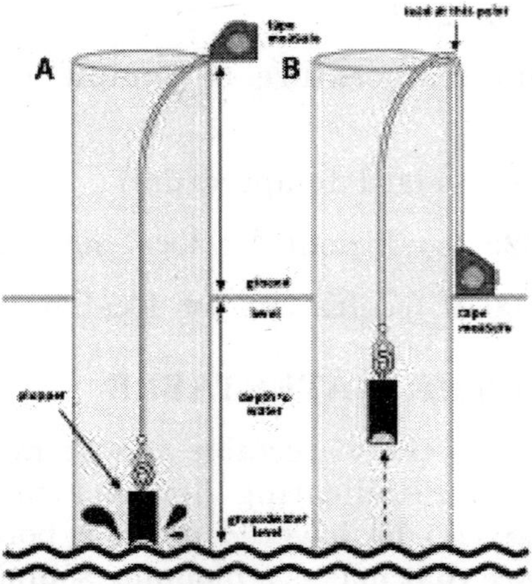

Figure 12.1. Using a plopper to measure depth to the watertable

jiggling the plopper up and down over a depth of about 50 mm until a plopping sound is heard every time the plopper is lowered. Obtain an accurate reading from the watertable to the top of the bore casing or piezometer by jiggling the tape less and less. Using this method, it is possible to accura-tely measure the depth to the watertable to within 5 mm.

- To correct for the height of the bore or piezometer casing, hold the tape at the top of the inner edge of the casing, and then pull the tape down to ground level. Now read the measurement on the tape at the top inner edge of the bore casing or top of piezometer.
- Add the distance between the end of the plopper and the beginning of the tape to the measure at the top of the bore casing. This will be an accurate measure of the depth to the watertable corrected for the height of the bore casing.

Use of Piezometers

Piezometers are very useful for assessing depth to the watertable, changes in water level with time and rainfall events, elevation of the watertable above a datum and hence the gradient of flow, estimated flow capacity of the aquifer material, chemistry of the water, and long-term monitoring of changes associated with land use.

To assess flow regimes and the interrelationships of aquifers, hydraulic head (the pressure of the groundwater) needs to be assessed. This is usually done using piezometers. By definition, a watertable level will not exceed ground level, whereas the hydraulic head associated with water in a confined aquifer (such as the Great Artesian Basin) may be many metres above ground level.

Piezometers measure pressure. The open well is a specialised type of piezometer which indicates the free water height of the watertable. Because water tends to flow from areas of high potentiometric potential to areas of low potential, water levels in piezometers are useful for indicating the direction of water flow.

The chemistry of dissolved salts in waters drawn from piezometers is useful for indicating the origins of the water and the chemical processes involved in determining the composition of the water. Information on the installation of the piezometers can be used in conjunction with water level information to determine aquifer hydraulic conductivity.

Other information is needed to obtain a comprehensive interpretation of the water level and chemistry information obtained from piezometers. This information includes:

- the bore log
- installation information, including depth, position and length of the slotted section of the tube and the sealing material
- rainfall records for the area (essential)
- elevation of each piezometer, preferably above Australian Height Datum or otherwise some arbitrary height reference
- any information from deep bores in the surrounding catchment
- observations of stream or spring flow, including water composition
- observations on land clearing or other human activities, such as dams, roads etc.

Installation

To obtain reliable information, piezometers must be installed correctly (Figure 12.2). In defective installations, water response may be slow, surface water could leak around the tube, or the sealing around the tube may be inadequate, so that the pressure head will be underestimated.

To determine the vertical direction of water movement at a particular site, a series of two or more piezometers (a 'nest') is sometimes installed. The nest of piezometers may be installed in separate holes or in the same hole with each individual piezometer terminating at a different depth, thus indicating the groundwater situation at each depth. Separate holes are preferred because the space around the piezometers can be sealed more effectively.

Siting

The design of piezometer installation will depend on the scale of the investigation. There are three broad types of installations:

1. **Exploratory**—a few piezometers are installed in selected areas to obtain a general picture of the area.
2. **Overall trends**—a broad network of piezometers is installed across and up the catchment and monitored in conjunction with existing bores and windmills (with the information from the existing installations being interpreted with caution).
3. **Hydrologic modelling** or detailed site analysis—a detailed network of piezometers is installed with piezometers set at several different depths and in all landform features in the catchment.

Drilling the Hole

Holes can be drilled using mechanical drilling rigs or alternative methods such as a hand auger or water jetting. A cutting head fitted with a replaceable tungsten carbide cutting tip is invaluable for drilling through occasional rocks as well as soil. Compressed air rock hammers may be required in hard rock. Isolated rocks (floaters) can give the impression that hard basement rock has been reached.

With experience, drill operators develop a feel for rock hardness and this, together with local knowledge and observation of material emerging from the drill hole, is an acceptable guide for hole depth.

The material brought up when holes are drilled provides valuable information about possible water pathways. It is important to keep a written log of observations while the holes are being drilled. Record any changes in the material (colour, texture, particle shape and size, concretions, wetness etc.), as well as the depth at which these changes occur.

When drilling in an unknown area, there may be aquifers at various depths. An exploratory hole is necessary to identify the relevant aquifers, not only the first encountered. Each aquifer may be tapped by a separate piezometer and it will usually be simpler to put these down separate drill holes.

Separate holes make it easier to seal the hole between the aquifers. It is important to seal immediately above the tapped aquifer, especially if it is below other aquifers.

Differences in water heights in piezometer tubes can indicate the presence of perched watertables or changes in the permeability of an unconfined aquifer.

Installing the piezometer

PVC pipe is recommended for the piezometer tube 40–50 mm in diameter, class 9 or 12. This tubing is robust and should withstand rough treatment during installation and operation. A section of the tube needs to be slotted to match the depth interval of the aquifer of interest. This is best done by hand, using a hacksaw frame fitted with two hacksaw blades spot-welded together to increase the thickness of the cut, or a power hacksaw can be used. Wider slots are recommended because thin ones can clog with fine material and restrict flow. As an alternative to slots, holes can be drilled in the tube. Record the length

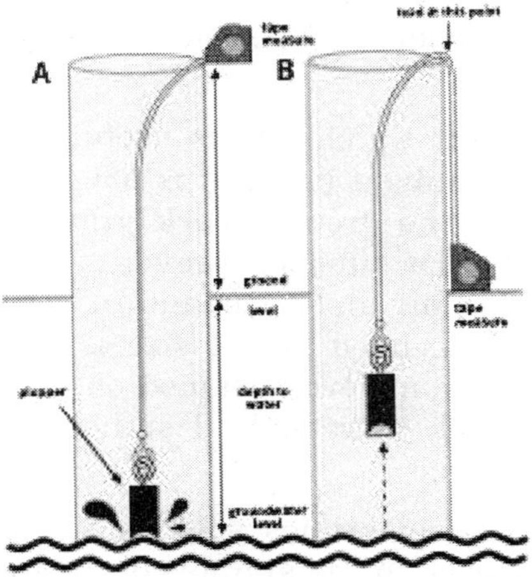

Figure 12.1. Using a plopper to measure depth to the watertable

of the slotted section before installing the tube in the ground.

If the drill hole remains dry or has little water in it after the drill is removed, installation should be straightforward.

In coarse sandy material, the piezometer tube can be jetted down with high pressure water. In rigid materials, water can be poured into the hole and the resulting slurry pumped out with a sludge pump. Jetting is another technique for clearing the hole—injecting compressed air down the piezometer tube as it is inserted so that material in the hole is lifted to the surface around the outside of the tube. This method is generally only effective if the slotted length of tube is relatively short.

In unstable materials, the walls of the hole may collapse, making installation more difficult.

Compressed air can sometimes be used to blow out slurried material but this can enhance the collapse of the walls. Jetting water down an open-ended piezometer tube can also be used to clear the hole but, depending on the material, this could reduce the permeability of the material around the slots.

A mirror or a flat watch face is useful for inspecting holes by reflecting sunlight (when it is not overcast). After setting the tube in the ground, pack gravel around the slotted section of the tube to prevent the hole from collapsing at this point and to maintain good hydraulic conductivity. Recommended gravel size is 5–7 mm river gravel (passing a 5 mm sieve, retained on a 7 mm sieve). With 5–7 mm gravel, there is still sufficient pore space to permit water flow.

Crushed metal (sometimes sold as gravel) has flat surfaces and may pack in the annulus of the tube. Coarser gravel can sometimes bridge around the annulus and block gravel falling to the bottom of the hole. The larger the gravel, the larger the pore space that will result. Coarse sand is more appropriate for sandy aquifer materials. Record the length of the gravel pack around the tube.

Above this gravel pack, a watertight seal is essential to prevent leakage into the tube from other aquifers (usually higher) or from the surface. The recommended material for sealing above the gravel pack is granulated bentonite. Carefully pour the bentonite around the tube to a depth of about 100 mm, and preferably top this with a shallow layer of gravel. In theory, where the water level is above the slotted section, the bentonite will settle through any water in the hole and swell to form a seal. However, sometimes the bentonite swells before reaching the desired position and air gaps are formed. A more reliable seal can be obtained by pumping the piezometer to lower the water level below the top of the gravel layer before pouring in the bentonite.

After the sealing layer is in place, backfill the rest of the hole to the surface and tamp the backfill into place.

Build up a mound of soil around the tube at the surface. Record details of sealing methods and depths.

The Piezometer above Ground

If the water level in the aquifer is not likely to rise above ground level, leave about 30-40 cm of the tube above ground level. This height is a compromise between being high enough for the site to be easily identified and low enough to limit damage from cattle, who often scratch themselves against the tube. The tube can be further protected from cattle by driving three steel pickets (painted for visibility) into the ground around the piezometer and wiring the stakes together. For more permanent installations, a steel protective casing can be concreted around the tube.

If the water in the aquifer is under considerable pressure with a hydraulic head above ground level, the water pressure may break through the bentonite seal. In this case, a longer tube will be needed, with appropriate support, and a cement grout should be used instead of bentonite.

Place a slip-on PVC cap onto the top of the tube. Ensure that there is a small hole in the cap or in the side of the tube near the top to relieve air pressure in the tube. Mark a unique identifying label inside the cap or the tube. Record this identification information with the other information on the installation of the tube.

Operation

By reading the water level in piezometers frequently during the first few months after installation, the response of the piezometer and an indication of likely future response can be determined. Information on the response of the water level to rainfall events is particularly useful. From this information, patterns of recharge and delayed response can be detected, used to interpret readings on a catchment scale, and related to soils, landforms and other features. Piezometer loggers, which can be obtained fairly cheaply, can be installed to obtain regular readings on changes in water level response.

To be able to assess flow directions, piezometer heights need to be surveyed to a common height datum. Because the elevation of the water surface (pressure head) is being surveyed, standard survey methodology can be used. If the head is higher in one piezometer than others, this does not necessarily indicate that water is flowing. Head differences usually indicate some restriction to flow.

Pump tests on piezometers can indicate flow rates in surrounding areas. There are a number of standard pump test procedures available, ranging from the simple bail tests and later modifications, to more detailed pumping schedules combined with taking measurements in surrounding piezometers. Interpreting pump tests, particularly in regions with strong geologic flow controls, can be difficult. Technical advice should be sought before carrying out these tests.

Catchment Groundwater Balance Estimation

An estimate of catchment water balance can be useful for initially assessing the magnitude of a salting problem, determining the most appropriate management options, and evaluating the amount of water to be managed in a salted catchment. Such an estimate will be rough because detailed hydrologic measurements are generally not available.

A complete catchment water balance would require measurements of runoff, evapotranspiration from existing vegetation, and deep drainage (groundwater recharge) as well as groundwater and surface water flow out of the catchment. Some of these measurements, particularly estimation of evapotranspiration using water balance models, require a considerable amount of land use data and are not sufficiently precise to accurately estimate deep drainage if this is less than 50 mm/yr. Estimating groundwater flow out of a catchment is also very difficult. Hence, the results of catchment water balance calculations need to be evaluated in the context of possible large errors.

Groundwater Balance Model

As discussed previously, groundwater recharge is balanced by discharge in the form of subsurface outflow, surface seepage, evaporation and evapotranspiration. Expressing this relationship in the symbols used to express quantities of water:

$$Q_d = Q_g + Q_s + Q_e + Q_t \tag{12.2}$$

This relationship can be expanded to incorporate measurable parameters for investigating groundwater balance:

$$D_d A_r = K_s \Delta H A_g + S + E A_b + ET\ A_v \tag{12.3}$$

where, using a time period such as a day,

Deep drainage rate ($D_d\ A_r$) (m^3/d) (volumetric rate at which water drains below the root zone, approximating recharge to groundwater) is the deep drainage rate (Dd) (m/d) by the area over which deep drainage (recharge) is occurring (Ar) (m_2)

Subsurface outflow from the discharge area ($K_s \Delta H A_g$) (m^3/d) is the potential of the aquifer medium to conduct water (K_s) (m/d), by the hydraulic gradient (ΔH) (m/m), by the cross-sectional area of the vertical discharge face of the aquifer at the lower catchment boundary (A_g) (m^2)

Surface seepage from the groundwater in the discharge area (S) (m^3/d) is the volumetric rate of water seeping from the groundwater in the discharge area, including base flow in drainage lines intersecting the discharge area (S) (m^3/d).

Evaporation from bare areas in the discharge area (EAb) (m^3/d) is the evaporation rate from bare areas per day (E) (m/d), by the amount of bare area in the discharge area (A_b) (m^2)

Evapotranspiration from vegetation in the discharge area (ET A_v) (m^3/d) is the evapotranspiration rate from vegetation in the discharge area per day (ET) (m/d), by the amount of vegetated discharge area (A_v) (m^2).

In some situations, aquifer parameters can be determined by conducting pump tests to determine transmissivity, which is the potential of a particular aquifer to transmit water per unit width. Hydraulic conductivity can be determined from transmissivity as follows:

$$K_s = \frac{T}{h} \tag{12.4}$$

where

K_s is saturated hydraulic conductivity (m/d)

T is transmissivity per unit width of aquifer ($m^3/m/d$)

h is thickness (vertical) of aquifer (m).

Using transmissivity information to calculate groundwater balance, the expression for the subsurface outflow component is modified as follows:

$$D_d\ A_r = Tw\Delta H + S + E\ A_b + ET\ A_v \tag{12.5}$$

where

T is the transmissivity of the aquifer per unit width (m^2/d)

w is the width of the aquifer at the point of subsurface outflow from the discharge area (m)

ΔH is the hydraulic gradient in the system (m/m).

WATER CHEMISTRY AND SALT SOURCES IDENTIFICATION

Laboratory analyses of water composition provide useful information for interpreting:

- likely sources of the water
- processes determining the composition (this is particularly so on a catchment scale if more than a few samples are available)
- possible uses of the water.

This information is also useful when deciding on appropriate management strategies.

Laboratory Analyses

Routine laboratory analyses are:

- soluble cations (Ca^{2+}, Mg^{2+}, Na^{+} and occasionally K^{+}) in meq/L, mg/L or mmole/L
- soluble anions (Cl^{-}, HCO_3^{-}, CO_3^{2-}, SO_4^{2-} and NO_3^{-}) inmeq/L, mg/L or mmole/L.

Electrical conductivity (EC at 25°C in dS/m) and pH are also measured in the laboratory. These tests, which can also be carried out in the field, have been described elsewhere. Calculations from the water analysis are made to estimate total dissolved ions (TDI) and sodium adsorption ratio (SAR).

Theoretically, a balance between the total number of positively charged ions (cations) and the total number of negatively charged ions (anions) is expected in the analysis of any water sample. In practice, due to analytical errors and/or the existence of species which, although present, are not measured, some degree of charge imbalance is likely. Usually, the results should be within ±5%. Large discrepancies indicate an unusual water or an error in the analysis.

Processes Controlling Ionic Composition

A natural water is an aqueous mixture of many components, the concentrations of which are controlled by complex and interrelated chemical processes as well as by the nature of the material the water has been moving over or through. Basic chemical processes and solubility of salts.

When water comes into contact with a mineral, dissolution begins and continues until equilibrium concentrations are attained or until all the mineral is consumed. This may take thousands of years if weathering is occurring, or days in the case of sparingly soluble salts. Thus, depending on the minerals encountered by natural waters, the salinity of natural waters can vary from only slightly more salty than rainfall to even more salty than seawater.

As the concentration of the solution increases, the EC does not linearly increase with salt concentration. This is because neutral ion pairs can form without any charge, such as $CaCO_3^0$ or $CaSO_4^0$, or with reduced charge, such as $CaHCO_3^+$. Gypsum is a classic example of this effect. The EC in dS/m is close to one-tenth of the concentration in meq/L (for example, 10 meq/L NaCl . 1 dS/m NaCl). For a saturated gypsum solution, however, 30 mmolec/L at saturation has an EC of 2.2 dS/m, due to ion pairing. Chemical analysis of a water assesses the total concentration of an element such as calcium and thus will give a higher salt reading.

The low solubility of calcium compounds is the reason for the prevalence of lime ($CaCO_3$) and gypsum in soils. Lime and gypsum are associated with salting in alkaline soil areas. In some regions, thick layers of lime are a good indicator of the presence of historic salting or wetness. Large gypsum crystals can be present in seawater-affected tidal areas.

Effect of CO_2 on Solubility of Carbonate Compounds

The partial pressure of CO_2 affects the solubility of carbonate compounds. Rainfall dissolving CO_2 from the atmosphere forms a weak acid (carbonic acid HCO_2^-) which is responsible for a considerable amount of rock weathering. This is particularly evident in limestone areas where flowing water can dissolve $CaCO_3$. In soils and groundwater, the partial pressure of CO_2 is greater than the atmospheric CO_2 partial pressure. In soils, this is due also to the effect of roots which increase the amount of CO_2. When waters with higher partial pressures of CO_2 are exposed to the atmosphere, there is a release of CO_2 (as in soft drinks) which can cause $CaCO_3$ to precipitate. Evaporation or evapotranspiration from a watertable fluctuating close to the soil surface can result in the precipitation of $CaCO_3$.

Total Salinity and Common Ion Effect

For some salts, as the total salt concentration increases (also called ionic strength) the solubility of the sparingly soluble salts increases. This is particularly the case when salts are dissimilar. For example, NaCl will enhance the solubility of $CaSO_4$. On the other hand, if the ions are the same, for example $CaCl_2$ and $CaSO_4$, or $MgSO_4$ and $CaSO_4$, there is a common ion effect where the amount of the less soluble salt in solution decreases.

Sources of Common Ions

Calcium

Calcium (Ca^{2+}) occurs in waters which have been in contact with igneous and metamorphic rocks containing the chain silicates (pyroxenes and amphiboles) and feldspars. In sedimentary rocks, calcium commonly occurs as carbonates, for example limestone which consists mainly of calcite with admixtures of magnesium and other impurities. Also, calcium carbonate can be present as a cement between particles in sandstone and other detrital rock.

The solubility of calcium in most natural waters is limited by processes involving carbon dioxide. The behaviour of calcium is generally governed by the availability of the more soluble calcium-containing solids and by solution- and gas-phase equilibria processes, or by the availability of sulfate anions.

Magnesium

In igneous rocks, magnesium (Mg^{2+}) is a constituent of the ferromagnesian minerals including olivines, pyroxenes, amphiboles and dark-coloured micas. Metamorphic rocks have magnesium-rich species such as chlorite, serpentine and montmorillonite. In sedimentary rocks, forms of magnesium include carbonates (magnesite), hydroxides (brucite) and calcium mixtures.

Magnesium carbonate solubility is more complex than that of calcium because of the many different forms of magnesium carbonates, hydroxycarbonates and hydroxides. Generally, these are more soluble than calcium carbonates.

Sodium

It has been estimated that feldspars make up about 60% of igneous rock minerals in the earth's outer crust. Calcium and sodium feldspars are relatively more susceptible to weathering than potassium feldspars. Acid igneous rocks (such as granite) contain higher proportions of sodium feldspars than basic igneous rocks (such as basalt), which contain higher proportions of calcium and magnesium feldspars.

In sedimentary rocks, sodium may be present in unaltered mineral grains, as impurities in the cementing material or as crystals of readily soluble sodium salts deposited with the sediments or retained following intrusions of sea water.

Sodium bicarbonate is the least soluble of the common sodium salts. At room temperature, a pure solution of this salt would contain around 1 642 meq/L of sodium. In natural waters, conditions favouring the precipitation of $NaHCO_3$ are unlikely to be attained. In general, the solubility of sodium is rarely exceeded in Australian waters. There is, however, some evidence of the presence of solid $NaHCO_3$ in some Burdekin soils. The presence of solid NaCl (halite) is unlikely in normal agricultural situations, as a saturated solution of NaCl can contain up to 6 108 mmolec/L of sodium and chloride. Precipitation of NaCl can occur in agricultural situations only where soil water, usually associated with shallow watertables, is concentrated at the soil surface by evaporation.

Sulfur

Sulfur (S) is not a major constituent of the earth's outer crust. However, sulfur is widely distributed, both in igneous and sedimentary rocks, as metal sulfides. Sulfur can also occur in certain igneous rock minerals of the felspathoid group. In sedimentary rocks, sulfides or pyrites are commonly associated with biogenic deposits such as coal. Evaporite sediments (such as gypsum) are another source of sedimentary sulfur. Sulfides can be oxidised by aerated waters to yield SO_4^{2-}. Sulfate is chemically stable in aerated waters. $CaSO_4$ is the least soluble common sulfate, with sodium and magnesium sulfates being many times more soluble.

Chloride

The chloride (Cl^-) content of rock minerals is generally very low. Residual water in pores or included within crystals of igneous rocks may be a source of chloride. More important sources are rainfall and sedimentary rocks where soluble chlorides may be present as a result of inclusion of waters in the sedimentary process. Porous rocks formed in the sea or submerged after their formation may also become impregnated with chloride salts.

Chloride in natural waters is not altered by oxidation/reduction reactions, does not form important solute complexes with other ions, does not form salts of low solubility, and is not significantly adsorbed onto mineral surfaces.

13

Water Quality

WATER QUALITY

Introduction

Irrigated agriculture is dependent on an adequate water supply of usable quality. Water quality concerns have often been neglected because good quality water supplies have been plentigul and readily available. This situation is now changing in many areas. Intensive use of nearly all good quality supplies means that new irrigation projects and old projects seeking new or supplemental supplies must rely on lower quality and less desirable sources. To avoid problems when using these poor quality water supplies, there must be sound planning to ensure that the quality of water available is put to the best use.

The objective of this chapter is to help the reader to a better understanding of the effect of water quality upon soil and crops and to assist in selecting suitable alternatives to cope with potential water quality related problems that might reduce production under prevailing conditions of use.

Conceptually, water quality refers to the characteristics of a water supply that will influence its suitability for a specific use, i.e. how well the quality meets the needs of the user. Quality is defined by certain physical, chemical and biological characteristics. Even a personal preference such as taste is a simple evaluation of acceptability. For example, if two drinking waters of equally good quality are available, people may express a preference for one supply rather than the other; the better tasting water becomes the preferred supply. In irrigation water evaluation, emphasis is placed on the chemical and physical characteristics of the water and only rarely are any other factors considered important.

Specific uses have different quality needs and one water supply is considered more acceptable (of better quality) if it produces better results or causes fewer problems than an alternative water supply. For example, good quality river water which can be used successfully for irrigation may, because of its sediment load, be unacceptable for municipal use without treatment to remove the sediment. Similarly, snowmelt water of excellent quality for municipal use may be too corrosive for industrial use without treatment to reduce its corrosion potential.

The ideal situation is to have several supplies from which to make a selection, but normally only one supply is available. In this case, the quality of the available supply must be evaluated to see how it fits the intended use. Most of the experience in using water of different qualities has been gained from observations and detailed study of problems that develop following use. The cause and effect relationship between a water constituent and the observed problem then results in an evaluation of quality of degree of acceptability. With sufficient reported experiences and measured responses, certain constituents emerge as indicators of quality-related problems. These characteristics are then organized into guidelines related to suitability for use. Each new set of guidelines builds upon the previous set to improve the predictive capability.

There have been a number of different water quality guidelines related to irrigated agriculture. Each has been useful but none has been entirely satisfactory because of the wide variability in field conditions. Hopefully, each new set of guidelines has improved our predictive capability. The guidelines presented in this chapter have relied heavily on previous ones but are modified to give more practical procedures for evaluating and managing water quality-related problems of irrigated agriculture.

Water Quality Problems

Water used for irrigation can vary greatly in quality depending upon type and quantity of dissolved salts. Salts are present in irrigation water in relatively small but significant amounts. They originate from dissolution or weathering of the rocks and soil, including dissolution of lime, gypsum and other slowly dissolved soil minerals. These salts are carried with the water to wherever it is used. In the case of irrigation, the salts are applied with the water and remain behind in the soil as water evaporates or is used by the crop.

The suitability of a water for irrigation is determined not only by the total amount of salt present but also by the kind of salt. Various soil and cropping problems develop as the total salt content increases, and special management practices may be required to maintain acceptable crop yields. Water quality or suitability for use is judged on the potential severity of problems that can be expected to develop during long-term use.

The problems that result vary both in kind and degree, and are modified by soil, climate and crop, as well as by the skill and knowledge of the water user. As a result, there is no set limit on water quality; rather, its suitability for use is determined by the conditions of use which affect the accumulation of the water constituents and which may restrict crop yield. The soil problems most commonly encountered and used as a basis to evaluate water quality are those related to salinity, water infiltration rate, toxicity and a group of other miscellaneous problems.

Water Quality-related Problems in Irrigated Agriculture

Salinity

Salts in soil or water reduce water availability to the crop to such an extent that yield is affected.

Water Infiltration Rate

Relatively high sodium or low calcium content of soil or water reduces the rate at which irrigation water enters soil to such an extent that sufficient water cannot be infiltrated to supply the crop adequately from one irrigation to the next.

Specific Ion Toxicity

Certain ions (sodium, chloride, or boron) from soil or water accumulate in a sensitive crop to concentrations high enough to cause crop damage and reduce yields.

Miscellaneous

Excessive nutrients reduce yield or quality; unsightly deposits on fruit or foliage reduce marketability; excessive corrosion of equipment increases maintenance and repairs.

Salinity

A salinity problem exists if salt accumulates in the crop root zone to a concentration that causes a loss in yield. In irrigated areas, these salts often originate from a saline, high water table or from salts in the applied water. Yield reductions occur when the salts accumulate in the root zone to such an extent that the crop is no longer able to extract sufficient water from the salty soil solution, resulting in a water stress for a significant period of time. If water uptake is appreciably reduced, the plant slows its rate of growth. The plant symptoms are similar in appearance to those of drought, such as wilting, or a darker, bluish-green colour and sometimes thicker, waxier leaves. Symptoms vary with the growth stage, being more noticeable if the salts affect the plant during the early stages of growth. In some cases, mild salt effects may go entirely unnoticed because of a uniform reduction in growth across an entire field.

Salts that contribute to a salinity problem are water soluble and readily transported by water. A portion of the salts that accumulate from prior irrigations can be moved (leached) below the rooting depth if more irrigation water infiltrates the soil than is used by the crop during the crop season. Leaching is the key to controlling a water quality-related salinity problem. Over a period of time, salt removal by leaching must equal or exceed the salt additions from the applied water to prevent salt building up to a damaging concentration. The amount of leaching required is dependent upon the irrigation water quality and the salinity tolerance of the crop grown.

Salt content of the root zone varies with depth. It varies from approximately that of the irrigation water near the soil surface to many times that of the applied water at the bottom of the rooting depth. Salt concentration increases with depth due to plants extracting water but leaving salts behind in a greatly reduced volume of soil water. Each subsequent irrigation pushes (leaches) the salts deeper into the root zone where they continue to accumulate until leached. The lower rooting depth salinity will depend upon the leaching that has occurred.

Following an irrigation, the most readily available water is in the upper root zone - a low salinity area. As the crop uses water, the upper root zone becomes depleted and the zone of most readily available water changes toward the deeper parts as the time interval between irrigations is extended. These lower depths are usually more salty. The crop does not respond to the extremes of low or high salinity in the rooting depth but integrates water availability and takes water from wherever it is most readily available. Irrigation timing is thus important in maintaining a high soil-water availability and reducing the problems caused when the crop must draw a significant portion of its water from the less available, higher salinity soil-water deeper in the root zone. For good crop production, equal importance must be given to maintaining a high soil-water availability and to leaching accumulated salts from the rooting depth before the salt concentration exceeds the tolerance of the plant.

For crops irrigated infrequently, as is normal when using surface methods and conventional irrigation management, crop yield is best correlated with the average root zone salinity, but for crops irrigated on a daily, or near daily basis (localized or drip irrigation) crop yields are better correlated with the water-uptake weighted root zone salinity. The differences are not great but may become important in the higher range of salinity. In this paper, discussions are based on crop response to the average root zone salinity.

In irrigated agriculture, many salinity problems are associated with or strongly influenced by a shallow watertable (within 2 metres of the surface). Salts accumulate in this water table and frequently become an important additional source of salt that moves upward into the crop root zone. Control of an existing shallow water table is thus essential to salinity control and to successful long-term irrigated agriculture. Higher salinity water requires appreciable extra water for leaching, which adds greatly to a potential water table (drainage) problem and makes long-term irrigated agriculture nearly impossible to achieve without adequate drainage. If drainage is adequate, salinity control becomes simply good management to ensure that the crop is adequately supplied with water at all times and that enough leaching water is applied to control salts within the tolerance of the crop.

Water Infiltration Rate

An infiltration problem related to water quality occurs when the normal infiltration rate for the applied water or rainfall is appreciably reduced and water remains on the soil surface too long or infiltrates too slowly to supply the crop with sufficient water to maintain acceptable yields. Although the infiltration rate of water into soil varies widely and can be greatly influenced by the quality of the irrigation water, soil factors such as structure, degree of compaction, organic matter content and chemical make-up can also greatly influence the intake rate.

The two most common water quality factors which influence the normal infiltration rate are the salinity of the water (total quantity of salts in the water) and its sodium content relative to the calcium and magnesium content. A high salinity water will increase infiltration. A low salinity water or a water with a high sodium to calcium ratio will decrease infiltration. Both factors may operate at the same time. Secondary problems may also develop if irrigations must be prolonged for an extended period of time to achieve adequate infiltration. These include crusting of seedbeds, excessive weeds, nutritional disorders and drowning of the crop, rotting of seeds and poor crop stands in low-lying wet spots. One serious side effect of an infiltration problem is the potential to develop disease and vector (mosquito) problems.

An infiltration problem related to water quality in most cases occurs in the surface few centimetres of soil and is linked to the structural stability of this surface soil and its low calcium content relative to that of sodium. When a soil is irrigated with a high sodium water, a high sodium surface soil develops which weakens soil structure. The surface soil aggregates then disperse to much smaller particles which clog soil pores. The problem may also be caused by an extremely low calcium content of the surface soil. In some cases, water low in salt can cause a similar problem but this is related to the corrosive nature of the low salt water and not to the sodium content of the water or soil. In the case of the low salt water, the water dissolves and leaches most of the soluble minerals, including calcium, from the surface soil.

Toxicity

Toxicity problems occur if certain constituents (ions) in the soil or water are taken up by the plant and accumulate to concentrations high enough to cause crop damage or reduced yields. The degree of damage depends on the uptake and the crop sensitivity. The permanent, perennial-type crops (tree crops) are the more sensitive. Damage often occurs at relatively low ion concentrations for sensitive crops. It is usually first evidenced by marginal leaf burn and interveinal chlorosis. If the accumulation is great enough, reduced yields result. The more tolerant annual crops are not sensitive at low concentrations but almost all crops will be damaged or killed if concentrations are sufficiently high.

The ions of primary concern are chloride, sodium and boron. Although toxicity problems may occur even when these ions are in low concentrations, toxicity often accompanies and complicates a salinity or water infiltration problem. Damage results when the potentially toxic ions are absorbed in significant amounts with the water taken up by the roots. The absorbed ions are transported to the leaves where they accumulate during transpiration. The ions accumulate to the greatest extent in the areas where the water loss is greatest, usually the leaf tips and leaf edges. Accumulation to toxic concentrations takes time and visual damage is often slow to be noticed. The degree of damage depends upon the duration of exposure, concentration by the toxic ion, crop sensitivity, and the volume of water transpired by the crop. In a hot climate or hot part of the year, accumulation is more rapid than if the same crop were grown in a cooler climate or cooler season when it might show little or no damage.

Toxicity can also occur from direct absorption of the toxic ions through leaves wet by overhead sprinklers. Sodium and chloride are the primary ions absorbed through leaves, and toxicity to one or both can be a problem with certain sensitive crops such as citrus. As concentrations increase in the applied water, damage develops more rapidly and becomes progressively more severe.

Miscellaneous

Several other problems related to irrigation water quality occur with sufficient frequency for them to be specifically noted. These include high nitrogen concentrations in the water which supplies nitrogen to the crop and may cause excessive vegetative growth, lodging, and delayed crop maturity; unsightly deposits on fruit or leaves due to overhead sprinkler irrigation with high bicarbonate water, water containing gypsum, or water high in iron; and various abnormalities often associated with an unusual pH of the water. A special problem faced by some farmers practising irrigation is deterioration of equipment due to water-induced corrosion or encrustation. This problem is most serious for wells and pumps, but in some areas, a poor quality water may also damage irrigation equipment and canals. In areas where there is a potential risk from diseases such as malaria, schistosomiasis and lymphatic filariasis, disease vector problems must be considered along with other water quality-related problems. Vector problems (mosquitoes) often originate as a secondary trouble related to a low water infiltration rate, to the use of wastewater for irrigation, or to poor drainage. Suspended organic as well as inorganic sediments cause problems in irrigation systems through clogging of gates, sprinkler heads and drippers. They can cause damage to pumps if screens are not used to exclude them. More commonly, sediments tend to fill canals and ditches and cause costly dredging and maintenance problems. Sediment also tends to reduce further the water infiltration rate of an already slowly permeable soil.

Approach to Evaluating Water Quality

The prediction that a water quality-related problem will occur requires evaluation of the potential of the water to create soil conditions that may restrict its use or that may require the use of special management techniques to maintain acceptable yields. There are a number of procedures available for this evaluation but regardless of which one is used, emphasis should focus on relating the potential problem to the field situation since solutions to water quality problems usually must be implemented at the farm level rather than at the project level. The evaluation must therefore be done in terms of specific local conditions of use and the farm management capability of the water user.

The four problem categories previously discussed - salinity, infiltration, toxicity and miscellaneous - are used for evaluation. Water quality problems, however, are often complex and a combination of problems may affect crop production more severely than a single problem in isolation. The more complex the problem, the more difficult it is to formulate an economical management programme for solution.

If problems do occur in combination, they are more easily understood and solved if each factor is considered individually. Therefore, the guidelines and discussion which follow treat each problem and its solution separately, so that a number of factors are evaluated for each of the problem areas, such as:

- the type and concentration of salts causing the problem;
- the soil-water-plant interactions that may cause the loss in crop yield;
- the expected severity of the problem following long-term use of the water;
- the management options that are available to prevent, correct, or delay the onset of the problem.

14

Human Activities

HUMAN LAND-USE AND RECORDS

Changes in land use over the period since development, when associated with the rainfall pattern over time, can indicate possible risk areas. Areas may have been abandoned for cropping for a number of reasons. To assess whether salinity was a factor, the suspect area should be analysed for landform and geological contributing features.

Sources of Information

There are a number of excellent sources of information on historical land use:

- Current and past landholders may be able to provide information about the history of the area, the timing and effects of clearing such as the development of local springs, and changes in water level and water quality in bores or wells.
- Sequential aerial photography—available from the 1940s in some areas and the 1920s in other areas—is available from DERM and, in some cases, the RAAF.

- Landsat imagery (for large-scale investigations) is available through Sunmap and other sources.
- Local historical societies and published histories of the local area often provide valuable information. When seeking information on land use over time and its effects, look for the following features in particular:
    - information about the property itself, as well as other properties in the same catchment, especially those upslope from the property in question
    - types and time periods of land use and why a particular land use (such as cultivation) was discontinued
    - patterns of clearing—which parts of the landscape were cleared, and when
    - patterns that indicate patchy growth or wet areas, and relationships with the rainfall pattern
    - areas where dams or weirs may have been built, even if these barriers no longer exist.

Interpretation

When analysing information on land use, consider whether the following effects, commonly associated with different land uses, have been in evidence in the area under investigation.

Cropping (Irrigated and Dryland)

Clearing land for crops can contribute to watertable and seepage salting when vegetation is removed which previously maintained the watertable at a depth below the soil surface where capillary rise was not significant. Fallow periods and some minimum tillage treatments can enhance recharge to the watertable. However, because of soil and aquifer characteristics, salting may not appear in the landscape until 20 to 50 years after initial clearing.

Under irrigation, the greater volume of water being introduced to the system can raise the watertable and lead to watertable and seepage salting. Under these conditions, salting may appear much sooner. Salts in irrigation water can contribute additional salts to soils being irrigated, causing irrigation water salting. This process can occur over periods of two to ten years. Increasing soil sodicity (which can result from using moderately to highly sodic water) also degrades soil properties.

When cropping practices leave the soil surface bare during periods of high rainfall or when the active growth period of the crop is too short to use the available water, the soil is vulnerable to erosion, contributing to erosion scalding on susceptible soils during major rainfall events.

Grazing (irrigated and dryland)

As for cropping, when land is cleared for pasture, vegetation is removed which previously maintained the watertable at depth below the soil surface. Salting may appear 20 to 50 years after initial clearing. Grazing lands in susceptible areas can be at risk of erosion scalding. When over-grazing in dry periods removes vegetation from the soil surface in areas with sodic subsoils, the soil is vulnerable to erosion scalding. Erosion scalding can also be seen around watering points, depending on how many there are and where they are positioned.

Residential Subdivision

Subdividing rural land into rural residential blocks can contribute to salinity in much the same way as land clearing and irrigation. When the development is occupied, increased amounts of water and nutrients are introduced into the system via wastewater and septic systems. Reticulated water supplies to developments, particularly those not serviced by sewerage, enhance recharge to groundwater and the likelihood of watertable salting in susceptible landscapes. However, compensatory managements, such as managed tree planting, enhanced use of groundwater (instead of reticulated water) and spray irrigation of properly treated waste effluent on an appropriately sized area, will assist in limiting watertable rise.

Roads and dams can become barriers to water movement or sources of additional water. Salting can occur upslope of roads and upstream or downstream of dams.

15

Management Issues

Management decisions are rarely straightforward or clear-cut because of the range of factors and complexity of interactions that contribute to salinity and determine management priorities:

- The expression of salinity in landscapes results from complex interactions between land use and management, landscape hydrology, geomorphology, historic salt loads, and socioeconomic and environmental factors.
- Because of the slow hydrologic response in many landscapes, there is often a long lead time between the expense and effort of implementing a management strategy and the subsequent enjoyment of the results.
- In some situations, the cost of implementing management strategies or controls can be greater than the value of on-site benefits or cost of off-site effects (although there is difficulty in assessing the full 'cost' of off-site effects).
- Property boundaries rarely encompass whole catchments, and additional problems can occur when

areas where the salinity problem is 'caused' and 'expressed' are controlled by different landholders.

The first step in developing an integrated, sustainable management strategy is to thoroughly investigate the processes and local factors contributing to salinity. Causal factors which have not been investigated and identified can not be addressed comprehensively and effectively.

After investigating salinity on-site and considering the available options in the light of the landholder's priorities, in the end the landholder must select a 'best bet' approach.

The best approach to watertable salting management is to view the water raising the watertable as a potential resource rather than as a problem, so that the situation can be managed to the landholder's net advantage. Depending on local circumstances and water quality, this water can possibly be diverted for productive use elsewhere on a property or in a catchment, to increase the productivity of existing resource uses or develop new uses, increasing revenue to the property and diversifying resource use.

Of the water inputs, only the water entering the recharge area is available to be managed. The salt concentration of this water is not readily amenable to management, but the quantity of the water can be managed by implementing strategies to reduce the proportion of water (rainwater and irrigation water) passing through the root zone. Reducing water inputs, wherever feasible, to maintain the watertable below the critical depth in the discharge area will have major benefits for the productivity of any vegetative management strategy for salt-affected lands, providing the salt concentration is still within the salt tolerance range of the vegetation. Other site parameters, such as the volume of groundwater flow and the sodicity of the groundwater, will influence final management options.

To effectively manage for productivity in the mediumto long-term in discharge areas affected by shallow watertables, evaporation needs to be reduced, particularly where there is very limited seasonal flushing of salts from the soil surface or the root zone by rainfall. If the water in this area can be reduced (by transpiration or pumping, or by interception before reaching the discharge area) to lower the watertable, salt can be stored in the unsaturated area at the bottom of the root zone where its effect is less significant. Salt in the root zone will be flushed by seasonal rainfall.

The only other viable option is to physically remove salt from the system. The option of discharging saline water into streams is generally not an acceptable practice. Another option, often not adequately addressed, is to remove water and salts by intercepting water moving in the transmission zone. This interception option is only viable where geologic features, soil conditions and water quality are favourable.

MANAGEMENT OPTIONS

A number of options for managing salt-affected catchments are available. Not all options are expensive to implement; one of the most common and useful is 'fence and forget'—fencing the area from stock and spelling it while natural or introduced salttolerant vegetation becomes established, after which time the area may be suitable for limited or controlled grazing.

Options for managing salted catchments, which can be used individually or in combination with other options, include:

- continuing with existing management—managing the land in its current state
- altering current management practices— considering alternative land uses (such as changing from cropping to pasture or trees), changing the grazing regime (such as resting areas by fencing them off from stock, or utilising an affected area as a gap feed rather

than for continuous grazing), and modifying existing irrigation practices

- selecting suitable vegetation species for planting in specific areas—establishing salt-tolerant pasture grass species and fodder shrubs in salt-affected areas, growing deep-rooted perennials such as lucerne or leucaena for fodder crops, considering alternative crops, and planting trees to intercept water in transmission areas or to use water in recharge areas
- retaining native vegetation—allowing native forest or perennial vegetation to revegetate naturally in recharge or discharge areas, and limiting future clearing of native vegetation on recharge areas
- implementing engineering options—installing drains or pumps to dewater areas with high watertables, using drainage systems to disperse water flow away from discharge areas, intercepting water in the transmission area by draining or pumping, and using intercepted water of suitable quality to irrigate crops or water stock.

Selecting an appropriate overall management strategy will depend on:

- the extent and nature of the salting problem
- the characteristics of the area—climate, soils, geomorphology, water quality, and so on
- access to unaffected areas that are contributing to the salinity problem (recharge and transmission areas)
- economic issues, such as the comparative value of the land and cost of implementing various management practices
- the landholder's own particular desires and needs.

Some strategies may be straightforward to implement while others may necessitate a complete reorganisation of farming operations. Catchment boundaries frequently cross property boundaries, with the result that neighbours may have to work cooperatively to effectively address the problem. Intensive engineering works or extensive tree planting programs may have to be staged over a number of years to suit available labour or financial resources.

INTEGRATED MANAGEMENT STRATEGIES

Broadly speaking, there are four potential management approaches for salt-affected lands. Each of these approaches aims to achieve a hydrologic balance between recharge and discharge areas:

- manage the existing situation
- reduce recharge
- intercept water in the transmission area
- increase water use in the discharge area.

In many situations, a combination of the four approaches may be needed to formulate the best salinity management strategy for local conditions and the available resources. Decision support tools such as property management models and benefit-cost analyses will assist in developing a balance between different levels of control in each of the recharge, transmission and discharge areas.

The relative size of recharge and discharge areas will determine, to some extent, which strategies may be appropriate. In any catchment, there has to be a minimum rate of drainage below the root zone to achieve a significant excess resulting in watertable rise. At minimum rates of drainage, vegetation can often cope with any additional water in the landscape. This can be approximated to around 0.001%. A maximum theoretical salt-affected area is around 10% of a catchment on the basis that the rate of evaporation from a discharge area can accommodate around 10 or more times the annual recharge rate. Surface seepage can also remove water from a catchment. In practice, this 10% is exceeded in southern Australia where there are widespread regional shallow watertables.

Manage the Existing Situation

This approach is appropriate where the salted area is of comparatively low-value land and natural processes prevent excessive salt from accumulating at the soil surface. For instance, the soil surface may be flushed on a seasonal basis by runoff or seasonal seepage. The key to this management option is to maintain adequate (and appropriate) vegetative cover at all times. Methods include fencing salt-affected areas and allowing opportunity grazing, and allowing weed or grass growth in cropping areas.

Reduce recharge

To reduce recharge, significant areas of the upper catchment may need to be revegetated with trees or well-managed native pastures, and agronomic practices in cropping areas may need to be substantially modified. Because recharge in many tropical areas is episodic, planting additional vegetation to reduce recharge will only be effective where water use by currently grown crops is low during the high rainfall season. Selecting appropriate vegetation options for recharge areas—whether or not to revegetate, whether to plant trees, crops or pasture—largely depends on the level of annual recharge. Intercept water in the transmission area

Water can be intercepted by revegetating key areas or by using engineering methods. If revegetating, groundwater needs to be present at depths that trees can access. Revegetation is more likely to be effective where water use by trees is likely to account for a significant proportion of the flow. If the water is of good quality, it can be reused elsewhere on the property for irrigation or stock watering. If aquifer properties and flow are suitable, water can be pumped from the transmission area using simple, lowtechnology, low-energy pumps.

Increase Water Use in the Discharge Area

Water use or removal by pumping, drainage and/or vegetation (with halophytes and salt-tolerant plants) is an option on discharge areas depending on the salt load and the depth of clay overlaying more permeable materials. Drainage requires permeable subsurface materials so that flow into the drains is adequate.

Clay depth provides a measure of the extent to which water can be removed by vegetation or engineering methods. Salt loads may be at shallow depths in some areas where upward hydraulic pressure operates. Under these conditions, a finite salt load exists that may be controlled by short-term high salt disposal or by managing the watertable level.

It is important that a drainage strategy does not lower the watertable to a critical depth which will actually result in an increase in the bare and salted area. In regions where salts are seasonally flushed from the soil profile by periodic high watertables, lowering the watertable to the critical depth for capillary rise can reduce the effectiveness of seasonal flushing. Surface concentration of salts will increase as a result.

Increased surface water flow from recently-installed drains may enhance gully erosion. The impact of increased salt loads on downstream water users must be considered, as well as environmental protection and water quality legislation.

MANAGEMENT DECISION-MAKING

Deciding how to manage a particular situation is rarely a case of simply choosing the option with the best prognosis. Many other factors enter into the decisionmaking process, and these factors will always depend on individual landholder priorities and constraints. Making salinity management decisions can mean deciding between competing objectives, such as economic and environmental objectives. While technical officers and other advisers provide expertise for assessing how particular areas will respond to different types of management, the final responsibility for deciding what will be done, and carrying out these decisions, lies with the individual landholders.

Broadly speaking, the following need to be considered when contemplating salinity management decisions:

- financial issues, such as set-up costs, comparative 'value' of amenity and aesthetics
- short- and long-term goals
- interest in diversification and alternative land uses
- personal attitudes to environmental responsibility
- potential for impact of a management strategy on properties downslope in the catchment
- activities and attitudes of neighbours and local catchment management groups.

Benefit-Cost Analyses

Benefit-cost analyses are invaluable when evaluating management strategies. Important considerations are the cost of managing the current degraded situation, costs of management for partial control, and costs of reclamation. For investigations of salinity risk before land is developed, the cost of preventative management for the area predicted to be affected will be required. Other considerations are the value of the productive lands in the recharge areas that may be reduced by some land management options such as revegetation. Management costs need to evaluate on-site versus off-site costs such as increased salinity of water supplies or increased erosion of salted areas, particularly in summer rainfall areas.

Decision Support Resources

Management decision support services range in scope from catchment-scale to property-scale. Community groups (for instance, landcare and Integrated Catchment Management groups and committees) help focus management strategies for salinity at the appropriate catchment scale. Using the principles of Property Management Planning, management decisions can be comprehensively worked through from initial investigation to implementation, ensuring the problem is thoroughly analysed and addressed and that a solution is determined that addresses the situation needs, is within the scope of available resources, and is consistent with personal and business goals and resource sustainability. With the increased number of stakeholders involved and more complex assessments of natural processes available, decision making is now a complex process.

Decision support system approaches are often necessary to provide a focus for the issues to be resolved. Decision support systems can be defined as 'the integration of expert knowledge, management models and timely information to assist in making day-to-day operational and long range strategic decisions'. Key concepts are the ability to evaluate 'what if' questions and to predict the effects of decisions. Where there are many stakeholders and multiple solutions, multidisciplinary approaches are required.

Because the rate of change in groundwater levels with time is often fairly slow, good predictions of the possible long-term consequences need to be made. Models are often necessary to adequately integrate climate variability (particularly rainfall) and spatial variability. However, models are only tools to assist understanding. A scaled approach in model complexity is required. Where the issues can be identified in yes/no terms, simple 'back of the envelope' calculations and expert opinion may suffice. Where the interactions between processes or managements are more complex, more quantitative, broad-scale and complex models with associated greater data requirements need to be considered. In all cases, as the catchment increases in size the accuracy of predictions will decrease sharply.

Catchment scale models, using well-developed groundwater models (for instance, MODFLOW) and incorporating decision theory allowing 'what if' situations to be evaluated, are currently being developed by the Department of Environment and Resource Management and CSIRO. Detailed modelling is generally time consuming and expensive, and is only justified when other management investigations are inconclusive.

Multi-objective decision support systems specifically addressing natural resource management issues are currently being developed. A wide range of agricultural productivity decision support systems are available. The following three approaches, PRIME, AEAM and MODSS, address aspects of natural resource management issues appropriate for catchment scale salinity issues.

PRIME (Planning, Research, Implementation, Monitoring and Evaluation) is a procedure for developing Integrated Catchment Management plans by stakeholder groups developed by the researchers. It is a staged decision framework. In the planning phase, the problem is defined, available knowledge collated, priorities formulated, objectives negotiated, gaps identified, the basic plan devised, and resources and criteria for evaluation and monitoring determined. In the research phase, feasible solutions from the literature and elsewhere are identified, barriers to adoption identified, and collaborative applied research programs developed. In the implementation phase, the implementation strategy is derived and resources determined and allocated for priority activities. Similar activities are carried out in the monitoring and evaluation phases.

The process is followed by a planning review phase in which coordination is a priority issue. This process is currently being used in a series of large catchments in Australia where integrated solutions to catchmentscale dryland and water salinity problems are being sought. PRIME is a decision support process rather than a software-based decision support system. The original AEAM (Adaptive Environmental Assessment and Management) concepts from Canada have been used at a catchment scale in some areas of Australia. The AEAM process aims to provide links between communities with a problem and the available technical resources. During a series of interactive workshops, a computer-based model is developed that can evaluate the outcomes of various resource management options using the best available technical information. The major benefits have been identified as the creation of a common understanding and ownership among stakeholders and the development of a computer simulation model using the best available information. Disadvantages are the need for skilled modellers in structured workshops and limited validation of the model except as a qualitative comparison with informed technical opinion. AEAM is suitable for some (but not all) situations and issues. Its usefulness depends on the time periods of the processes and the extent to which catchment scale averaging of biophysical responses provides acceptable data.

A multi-objective decision support system (MODSS) is available (prototype currently) that allows individuals and groups to identify the issues, the stakeholders, the criteria and the importance ranking in order to select the most appropriate option. The system will produce a number of options together with a matrix of options against criteria to be rated from a range of sources, data, technical experts and simulation models. Following decision optimisation techniques, the preferred options can be considered, discussed and resolved. Further information on MODSS can be obtained from the Department of Environment and Resource Management.

16

Vegetation Management

Vegetation can be planted (or retained) to manage water:

- by reducing recharge to the groundwater
- by intercepting water as it moves through the landscape
- by increasing the rate of groundwater discharge.

Vegetation in Areas of the Landscape

Careful planning is the key to cost-effective treatment of salinity. Approaches integrating vegetation with engineering works and modified farming practices are most likely to be successful.

It is generally better to focus vegetation management on transmission and recharge areas than discharge areas. This is because the high salt concentrations in the soil and groundwater in discharge areas, often accompanied by seasonal waterlogging and the presence of sodic soils, create unfavourable conditions for plant survival and growth. The effectiveness of increasing vegetative extraction of saline groundwater in the discharge area alone (without reducing recharge) is limited because:

- it is difficult to establish plants in saline environments
- the rate at which plants use water depends on the stress they experience
- the amount of water supplied by the comparatively extensive recharge area will usually be far in excess of the transpiration capacities of vegetation planted on the discharge area, even if all the vegetation were using water at the optimal rate
- special management of the area will be required for long-term stability
- the removal of water by transpiration may increase soil salinity levels and aggravate the problem of insufficient water use.

Vegetation in the discharge area is appropriate for managing erosion and maintaining some productivity. Unless the supply of water to the discharge area is reduced, a permanent reduction of the problem is not likely to be achieved by vegetation in the discharge area alone.

The information in the following sections on species selection applies generally to selecting pasture, crop and tree species for managing salinity in summer rainfall areas. Species to be planted in recharge, transmission or discharge areas that are adapted for the general site conditions will improve the likelihood of survival and growth without requiring excessive maintenance during periods when conditions are unfavourable.

Recharge areas

In recharge areas, trees and high water use crops can reduce deep drainage by using more water to a greater depth and by intercepting more rain in the canopy than most pastures or crops, especially in winter rainfall areas. In summer rainfall areas, summer fallow and heavily grazed pastures will result in increased recharge. Opportunity cropping and pasture systems which include some deeper rooted species will reduce recharge to some extent.

The soil water available to plants in recharge areas is not usually saline and thus the normal species selection factors for local site conditions will indicate the long-term growth of the chosen species. Ideally, species with high water use capability are preferred. Factors to be considered in selecting species for recharge area plantings are:

- site conditions—rainfall, risk of frost, exposure to winds and sun, soil types, existing vegetation, original vegetation type
- species water use capability
- in the case of trees, multiple use considerations—possible use for timber production, stock shade or shelter, windbreaks, wildlife habitat, or tree products such as honey, bush tucker, flowers, oils or seed.

Transmission Areas

Transmission area plantings can be an effective option when good quality groundwater is moving through the landscape in a zone accessible to plant roots. For instance, access by plant roots to the groundwater should not be impeded by structures such as hard pans or other geological formations.

If groundwater in the transmission area is saline, transmission area plantings may be ineffective. Water uptake is likely to decrease over time as salt becomes concentrated in the root zone, thus reducing the effectiveness of vegetation in removing groundwater. A rough calculation of catchment water balance is needed to see if the area planned for revegetation can use sufficient water.

Conditions in transmission areas are often similar to those in recharge areas, possibly with higher levels of groundwater salinity. In some cases, transmission areas can have more favourable conditions for vegetation establishment than recharge areas because of better groundwater supplies or better soils on lower slope positions.

Species should be chosen on the basis of high water consumption capacity and the ability to cope with moderately saline groundwater (if present) and saline soils (which may occur over time). Multiple uses of trees would be important secondary considerations. Consideration could be given to species that can be irrigated with low to moderate salinity groundwater supplied by groundwater pumping.

DISCHARGE AREAS

As discussed previously, vegetating discharge areas effectively can be difficult. However, planting discharge areas with salt- or water-logging-tolerant vegetation can be important when recharge areas are hard to identify, difficult to manage or revegetate sufficiently to control recharge, or unavailable for management (for instance, if the recharge area is on another property).

Discharge area plantings provide an opportunity for bringing an area of land back into productive use. Many landholders prefer to focus remedial vegetation activity on the unproductive salted sites rather than to place productive agricultural uplands under alternative vegetation.

Combined with other planting or engineering works, discharge area plantings may lower the watertable sufficiently to prevent further concentration of salt on the soil surface by evaporation and to allow leaching of surface salt by rainfall, enabling more productive use of the site. Naturally saline soils support a diversity of species, some of which are useful agronomically. If vegetation strategies are well planned and managed, saline soils can be productive.

Factors to be considered when choosing species for planting on discharge sites, usually very harsh environments, are:

- adaptation to the general site conditions
- salinity tolerance
- sodicity tolerance
- tolerance to poor soil drainage or waterlogging
- frost tolerance
- water use capability
- potential for multiple use (in the case of trees).

These factors often occur in combination, and this usually has a compounding impact on vegetation, young plants in particular. A more restricted range of species is likely to be available and opportunities for multiple use will be limited as plants are unlikely to perform well under highly saline or waterlogged conditions.

General Site Conditions

Adaptation to climate, soils, aspect and other factors has to be considered more carefully when choosing plants for the adverse conditions of discharge areas than for areas with favourable growing conditions.

Salinity Tolerance

Many plant species are unaffected by relatively low soil salt concentrations. Some species can withstand moderate or high salinity levels. Relatively few species are able to tolerate very high levels of salt. Even where a species can survive in saline conditions, growth rates and resistance to disease may be severely retarded.

If irrigation with groundwater is proposed, a species' ability to tolerate irrigation with saline water may also need to be considered.

Sodicity Tolerance

Many saline sites are also sodic. Plant species vary in their ability to tolerate sodic soils. The major constraints to plant growth in sodic soils are:

- poor physical conditions and correspondingly poor soil aeration when wet
- nutritional imbalances including deficiencies of trace elements
- specific ion toxicity (such as sodium, chloride or possibly boron).

Tolerance of Poor Soil Drainage or Waterlogging

Species adapted for dealing with poor drainage or waterlogging will usually be more successful in discharge areas. Some species can tolerate seasonal waterlogging, sometimes for many months, but many species are highly intolerant of these conditions. Waterlogging usually reduces the ability of plants to tolerate saline conditions, so species that can survive a combination of salinity and waterlogging are often required. If watertables are consistently high, trees may form very shallow root systems, making them susceptible to windfall.

Frost Tolerance

Saline discharge areas usually occur in the lowest parts of the landscape, where there is poor drainage of the cold air. If frosts occur in the area, frost-hardy species may be required.

Water Use

Water use capability is an important factor when selecting species for discharge areas. However, in harsh conditions this factor will be secondary to selecting species that can survive on the site. Tree spacing and management can be used to some extent to affect the amount of water use in a planted area. Water use is determined by species, climate and local environmental factors.

Multiple Uses

The economics of saline site rehabilitation improve substantially if financial returns can be obtained from trees used in the rehabilitation process. If suitable matches can be made between tree species, site conditions, products and services, and good integration can be achieved between agricultural enterprises and tree management systems on the property, a high economic return can be obtained from landscapes supporting a large percentage of tree cover. Trees may also contribute services to the farm in terms of wildlife habitat, shade and shelter for crops and stock, and aesthetic value.

General site treatment

Many pasture, crop and tree species are most sensitive to salinity at germination and during establishment. Even species able to grow in extreme levels of soil salinity, such as saltbush, normally germinate and establish only after rain has flushed salts from the soil surface. Soil preparation methods and activities that reduce surface salt levels and promote plant growth are therefore vital for successful establishment of plants in saline environments.

Vegetative Cover

In almost all areas susceptible to salting, the vegetative cover of the soil surface needs to be maintained and the soil surface not laid bare by cultivation or overgrazing. Where salting is associated with a shallow watertable, removing vegetation from the soil will lead to the surface accumulation of salts. In areas susceptible to scalding, a bare soil surface will be vulnerable to erosion processes, soil loss and soil degradation.

Mulching is beneficial because it reduces concentration of salts at the soil surface and aids plant establishment.

Grazing and Stock Control

Grazing and pest animals must be controlled by fencing or low stocking rates for pasture or tree planting or regeneration to be successful. In many cases, grazing control alone on the affected area and margins is sufficient to allow salt-affected areas to revegetate successfully. Costs include the cost of fencing and loss of amenity of the fenced-off area. Benefits include preventing the spread of the salting problem and being able to use the area again to some extent after revegetation.

Water Movement Control

The areas to be reclaimed should be protected from runoff water. A diversion bank can be used to direct water to more stable areas. Planting is best carried out at the beginning of the wet season when watertable levels are lowest and early rains have flushed salt from the surface.

Mounding

If the soil water is saline, trees, crops and pastures planted on the tops of standard mounds can be affected by evaporative salt accumulation at the high point of the mound. This effect can be minimised by using mulch, constructing broad mounds, and setting the plants off the top of the mound. Seedlings planted in the trough of M-shaped mounds are less likely to be affected by salinity because salt will accumulate in the peaks to either side of the trough.

There is mixed evidence on the benefits of forming mounds some time prior to planting. In M-shaped mounds, water collecting in the trough of the mound may leach some salt from the soil. However, capillary action and evaporation from the increased bare area of soil may bring additional salt into the mound. In standard-shaped mounds constructed prior to planting, salt accumulation in the mound can be a problem if insufficient rain falls to leach salts. Soil leaching can be achieved without salt accumulation if the mounds are mulched.

Vegetation Options

A number of factors need to be considered when deciding whether and where to use crops, pasture or trees to manage salinity:

- landholder's goals—importance of initial cost and final financial return, time available to manage
- individual area characteristics—water source, water quality, landscape feature to be planted, soil characteristics, soil salinity and sodicity levels
- individual species characteristics—salt tolerance, water use, rooting depth, time to establishment, likely productivity
- time frame before a response will be evident—interaction between climate (period of dominant rainfall) and time to establishment of species.

Pasture

The following situations are more suitable for pastures than cropping:

- low-value land
- strongly undulating country or steep slopes
- soils of moderate to high permeability
- where soil acidity is not a limiting problem

- where deep-rooted or perennial grasses are viable
- if grazing gives viable returns
- if grazing control can be effected
- when agroforestry is an option
- when climate and/or water resources favour pastures.

Crops

Few traditional crops can be grown on saline soils. High water use crops can play a role in recharge control. Situations most suited to using crops to manage salinity include:

- soils of moderate to high fertility and low salinity
- soils with good plant-available water capacity
- soils have moderate to high clay content
- soils have low to moderate hydraulic conductivity
- soil erosion can be controlled
- areas suitable for cultivation
- where opportunity cropping in wetter years is an option
- where cropping practices, including fallow practices, can be managed to minimise recharge.

Trees

Under favourable conditions, trees can extract large quantities of water from the soil by transpiration and can directly intercept and evaporate rainfall. Trees actively use water for a greater part of the year than most crops and pastures. When planted in recharge areas, trees use more water to a greater depth in the root zone than shallower rooted species, reducing deep drainage. When planted in transmission and discharge areas, some tree species can draw water directly from the groundwater. However, less than favourable conditions in discharge areas are not optimal for timber production. Trees may also contribute less directly to salinity control by:

- providing shade and shelter on discharge areas, and reducing surface evaporation rates and the rate of concentration of salt at the soil surface
- assisting to reduce the risk of wind and water erosion on scalded sites by acting as windbreaks, providing a litter mulch, reducing raindrop energy and binding the soil with root systems.

Situations most suited to using trees to manage salinity include:

- shallow soils over weathered and fractured rock
- deep sandy or permeable soils
- steep and broken country
- where timber processing industries are situated nearby
- when shade or windbreaks are needed
- when wildlife protection is desired
- if agroforestry is an option.

PASTURE

A variety of palatable and nutritious forage plants can be established on saline soils provided appropriate species are selected and management regimes adopted. Pastures on saline areas are most valuable if crash-grazed followed by a long spell. This allows pastures to recover and the salt-affected area to be utilised as a gap feed.

Pasture Species

The legumes *Medicago sativa* cv. Sirosal, *M. scutellata, M. truncalata, Macroptilium lathyroides, M. atropurpureum* and *Trifolium fragiferum* tolerate mild salinity but are usually more difficult to establish . With all of these species, local suitability must be assessed.

Forage shrubs such as saltbush can raise the feed value of mixed pastures on saline soils. Saltbush, bluebush and related plants have been considered a valuable stabilising component of grazing pastures in arid and semiarid areas of Australia for many years because of their ability to maintain green leaf through seasonal dry spells and droughts. Closer to the coast, these species are valuable for grazing during dry periods, as their protein levels are maintained when other feeds have hayed off. It is necessary to have alternative feeds available (crop stubble, grasses) to dilute the high salt content of the shrubs. Some species do not tolerate waterlogging. Species which are known to grow well on saline soils, be palatable to stock, and withstand grazing pressures are indicated in the table in the appendix Pasture species for saline soils (page 133).

Samphires and glassworts are valuable in areas where extreme salinity and regular waterlogging prevent the growth of other plants. The protein content of samphire is high, but intake is reduced by salt levels of about 20% dry weight of chloride. These species may improve soil conditions such that other, lesstolerant species can establish through them.

Pasture Establishment and Maintenance

Pasture Cultivation

Shallow cultivation is normally sufficient to establish pasture species and grasses. Deep ripping and agroplough are only justified if significant yield improvement is obtained as a result. It is not always necessary to spray or burn existing weed species to allow desirable species to establish successfully.

Pasture Planting

Many of the grasses used on salt-affected soils in Queensland can only be established from rooted clumps or turf. A sprig planter can be used for planting grasses such as marine and saltwater couch. If planting by hand, a shallow hole should be dug into which the grass clumps are pressed.

For species to be introduced by seed, shallow cultivation of the soil surface to dilute salts through the top few centimetres of soil is generally sufficient for establishment. Pioneer Rhodes grass establishes well from seed on highly saline soils; more palatable species included in the seed mix may be able to establish after Pioneer Rhodes.

On flat ground, a conventional combine without harrows can be used to provide variety in the soil surface. A scarifier can be useful immediately prior to sowing on highly saline soils. Seed is spread on the surface. On steep slopes, where cultivation is not recommended because of the risk of erosion, direct drill seeding may be appropriate provided the seed is not buried too deep. If machinery access is not practical, for example on waterlogged sites, spreading seed by hand on the soil surface is sufficient.

Saltbushes can be established from either seed or nursery-raised seedlings. Success rates are much higher if seedlings are used, but costs also increase. Double ridge or M-shaped mounds are advisable to flush salts from the root zone of the young seedling to reduce transplanting shock. Mounds are also recommended for spot placements of seed covered by a mulch such as hay or vermiculite. The Mallen niche seeder can be used for this purpose.

Optimal plant spacing varies between species; spacing should allow for sufficient grass growth between the bushes to provide a balanced diet. River saltbush (*Atriplex amnicola*) is best planted at 1000 plants/ha, whereas grey saltbush (*Atriplex cinerea*) is best planted at 125 plants/

ha. Saltbush productivity can be improved significantly by using an agroplough and a nitrogen fertiliser such as DAP.

Samphires are best established from seed sown on the surface. Seed can be spread by harvesting plant shoots soon after seeding and spreading these pieces. Coastal pigface (*Sesuvium portulacastrum*) establishes well from plant pieces.

Fertilising

To improve the condition of low sodicity/high salinity soils, gypsum can be applied before cultivation at a rate of 5 to 7 t/ha. However, if high levels of soluble salts are also present, gypsum will have little effect. Gypsum is recommended for clay soils with low salinity. Early in the following growing season, the area should be top-dressed with complete fertiliser 4:4:1 of NPK at 125 kg/ha. Local extension advice will be available on general fertiliser use.

Mulching

Mulching normally promotes grass establishment in salt-affected areas. Hay, straw or manure can be used. Grass hay is normally more suitable than cereal hay as seeds of undesirable species in grass hay are less likely to survive under saline conditions.

Grazing Control

Stock should be excluded for at least 12 months and up to two years after salt-tolerant species are planted. Such areas can be grazed subsequently for short periods of time. Saltland pastures are most valuable when used as a feed reserve when other pastures are in short supply and spelled for the remainder of the year.

CROPS

In recharge and transmission areas, crop type and cropping systems should be selected to maximise water use and minimise fallow and dormant periods. As with pastures, it is appropriate to limit discussion here to cropping on marginal and salt-affected soils. Choosing crop species for recharge and transmission areas will relate more to soils and climate that to salinity as such.

On marginal soils, cropping can be viable if appropriate species are selected and careful management is practised. Extensive breeding programs have been conducted in an attempt to raise the salt tolerance of many crop species, but results have been largely disappointing. This is because traditional food crops, other than beets and date palms, are not halophytic and thus have relatively low salt tolerance.

Crop Species

Species selected to tolerate the highest expected levels of salinity will be likely to produce the best yields. It is also important to recognise that salt tolerance varies with the growth stage of plants. Some species are more salt tolerant at germination and emergence than after establishment. While 50% yield and 50% emergence are used for comparative purposes, cropping is not economically viable at these levels of reduction.

Crop Establishment and Maintenance

In saline areas, evaporative concentration of salt on the soil surface or in the upper root zone is the most likely cause of poor crop response. Maintaining any amount of stubble on the soil surface will help to reduce evaporation. Minimum tillage practices and seeding into previous crop residues can also help to reduce evaporation.

By planting into the trough of M-shaped ridges or into the side of single-humped ridges, plants can be separated from the ridge peaks, where maximum evaporative salt concentration occurs. However, if these practices are necessary, it may be more economically viable to move from crops to pasture.

Periodic irrigation to flush salts from the soil surface can effectively reduce salt loads where soils are permeable and watertables are deeper than about 0.5 m.

TREE PLANTING

Using trees to manage salinity is a long-term strategy. After trees are planted, it will be some years before watertable levels start to be affected and many years before the trees reach maturity and provide other desired benefits. The use of trees in salinity control should be consistent with property management aims and objectives and be integrated with other farm management activities so that the trees can be properly managed and maintained in the long term. Trees can be used to enhance the farm environment, boost returns from established enterprises and provide opportunities for diversification into forestry or forest products.

Shade and shelter produced by trees can improve growth rates in stock, increase calving and lambing percentages, extend the availability of pasture in times of drought or frost, and reduce soil-water consumption by crops. Use of *Acacia* spp. on discharge sites or fodder species such as leucaena on recharge areas can provide high protein browse for stock, increasing productivity compared with pasture alone. Many tree species produce valuable timber and wood products such as firewood, fencing timber, poles and sawlogs for structural or decorative purposes, veneer logs, and craft timbers. Many Eucalyptus and Acacia species suitable for salinity control are premiumquality structural and appearance-grade timbers.

Some species of eucalyptus, tea tree and brush box are sought by beekeepers because of the excellent honey produced. Other tree products are fruits and nuts, oils, substances for medical use, flowers, bush tucker and seed.

Mallee and Melaleuca species can be harvested for oil production. By selecting a diverse range of tree and shrub species for windbreaks and shade, a variety of food sources and nesting and shelter opportunities can be provided for native bird, mammal, reptile and invertebrate species.

Costs associated with tree planting generally include costs of tree establishment (fencing, site preparation) and maintenance, costs of lost agricultural production on the planted area, and cost of time spent away from other farming activities. Benefits of tree planting include returns to the landowner as well as to the community. Community benefits are in the form of reduced impact on downstream water quality, increased habitat values and improved salinity control on neighbouring properties.

Where trees are planted (or maintained) primarily to prevent or combat land degradation, such as to control salinity, stabilise erosion gullies, and establish windbreaks to prevent soil erosion, associated costs may have tax advantages. If trees are planted for the purpose of producing timber, associated costs are deductable as business-related expenses. Resubdivision of the property according to land types is also deductible if it is carried out in accordance with an approved farm plan.

Appropriate reforestation layouts and attention to the choice of species can ensure that an optimal economic return is achieved. Comprehensive economic analysis of farm operations, comparing the status quo with strategic options, will allow the most economically efficient strategy to be selected. Computer-based models can facilitate this analysis.

Tree Species

Vegetation on the site and remnant native vegetation on similar sites in the area can indicate suitable species. However, if there have been extensive changes to the landscape (clearing, modification of soils by pasture improvement, cultivation or the addition of fertilisers), local species may no longer be the most suitable.

Tree Establishment and Maintenance

Site Planning

In most situations, a mixture of recharge, discharge and transmission area plantings will be required if trees are to be used in salinity control. Layout must be planned considering the hydrology and stratigraphy of the site, salinity, waterlogging, soil fertility and opportunities to integrate tree plantings with other property enterprises or to obtain products and benefits directly. The cost of fencing off young trees from stock (which is potentially considerable) can be reduced by integrating planting patterns with existing fencing layouts, if possible.

Options for recharge area plantings range from broad-scale revegetation of a significant proportion of the recharge area to intensive plantations of high water use trees on high recharge areas. Optimal performance will be obtained by planting trees at a density that allows each tree to develop a full canopy with a high leaf area index and an extensive root system. This suggests that wide-spaced agroforestry plantings may be very effective in grazing areas, while linear windbreaks may be appropriate in cropping and mixed farming areas. To bring the area back into agricultural production relatively quickly, trees can be planted densely to lower the watertable and later thinned to allow pasture to establish. Widely spaced large trees with well-developed root systems continue to use water at a high rate because of good air flow around the tree crowns.

The optimal amount of area for tree planting will vary from site to site, depending on local rainfall and aquifer characteristics. However, evidence from Western Australia indicates that replanting less than 15% of the recharge area is ineffective, and that effectiveness is directly proportional to the area planted. Increasing effects have been observed from planting larger proportions of cleared recharge areas, with the effect being proportional to the area of land replanted. However, this is likely to be highly variable depending on groundwater hydrology and rainfall characteristics and the results cannot be extrapolated to areas with different conditions.

In transmission areas where conditions are suitable, intensive plantations or belts of trees may be a costeffective way of removing groundwater without using the large areas of land needed for recharge area plantings.

In discharge areas, tree planting is only appropriate where revegetation of a large enough area to use considerable amounts of groundwater relative to that flowing into the area can be achieved. In many cases this may mean using discharge area plantings in conjunction with other management strategies, such as engineering methods, to reduce groundwater recharge or to intercept water before it reaches the discharge area. The tendency of trees to concentrate salt in the root zone is likely to be a problem only in low rainfall areas where insufficient rain falls to periodically flush salt from the soil profile.

Site Preparation

Under normal conditions, cultivation benefits young trees by improving root penetration and water infiltration and controlling weeds. However, on waterlogged sites, cultivation can exacerbate the waterlogging problem because heavy machinery compacts wet soil. On well-drained sites with clay subsoils, deep ripping can be useful to improve soil drainage and root penetration. The best time for deep ripping is winter or spring (as late as possible in the dry season) when the ground is least waterlogged and soils are at an optimal moisture content for penetration and shattering. Rip lines should be strip sprayed with a combination of knockdown and residual herbicides.

Gypsum can be added to improve soil permeability during tree establishment in areas with clay soils, poor soil drainage or waterlogging, or high pH or sodicity levels.

Mounding benefits tree survival and early tree growth on most saline and/or waterlogged sites. M-shaped mounds (with a small indentation along the top) are generally better for alleviating salinity problems, and standard (single-humped) mounds are better for waterlogging problems. Surface drains (furrows) formed while creating mounds should be aligned to maximise surface water drainage from the site.

Initial tree survival and early growth is likely to be improved if, prior to planting, salt can be leached from the soil (for instance, by using drip irrigation or plastic mulch on M-shaped mounds with holes punched for planting positions) without adding to waterlogging problems. Other methods of reducing topsoil salinity, such as mixing saline topsoil with less saline subsoil using deep cultivation, adding less saline soil to planting holes, or mixing organic matter with saline topsoil, appear to provide limited benefit and are not cost-effective.

Tree Planting

On moderately saline sites with good drainage, the best time to plant is most likely after early summer rainfall has provided sufficient soil moisture. Planting at this time will maximise growth during the available growing season and provide shading and soil cover in the shortest possible time. In areas prone to seasonal waterlogging, planting should be carried out as soon as the area ceases to be waterlogged following the end of the wet season to allow the seedlings maximum time to become established before the next wet season. On severely salt-affected sites, the optimum time to plant may be after a period of high rainfall which will have flushed some salt from the soil surface and upper soil profile.

Survival can be improved by preconditioning seedlings to site conditions such as waterlogging and salinity. Gradual exposure to increasingly waterlogged conditions in the nursery appears to be the most effective part of this preconditioning.

Fertilising is generally recommended for tree planting projects, but good weed control is essential. At planting, 100 g of DAP or an equivalent N–P fertiliser may be applied to each seedling. However, as stressed trees growing on waterlogged or saline sites may be less able to utilise additional nutrients, fertiliser should generally only be added when trees are not suffering waterlogging or salinity stress.

Mulching improves tree survival, increases growth rates, improves soil moisture conditions and reduces salinity levels in the soil beneath mulch. The choice of mulch will usually depend on availability and cost. Effective material for mulch is sometimes available as a by-product of other farming activities. Trees need to be watered well at the time of planting as for any planting project. Enhanced growth rates, improved productivity and more rapid lowering of watertables may be achieved if tree plantings can be irrigated with suitable quality groundwater.

Tree Maintenance

Fencing to control animal access is critical on saline sites, both to prevent browsing damage by grazing stock or feral animals while trees are young and to control grazing of pastures on the site in the long term.

Trees stressed by growing in waterlogged or saline conditions are vulnerable to insect attack. The severity of insect attacks can be reduced in some instances by revegetating additional areas in the vicinity of the areas being treated for salinity. Insect pest problems will be minimised if a diverse range of native species is planted in an area to maximise the variety of habitats available.

Control of weeds (including grasses and pastures) around trees for a distance of about 1.5 m from the base of the tree for the first 12 to 18 months is generally necessary for good tree survival and growth. Weed control options include cultivation, hand weeding, mulching and the use of knockdown and residual herbicides.

Slashed or graded fire breaks 5 to 10 m wide should be maintained around planted areas. Slashing between rows of trees will minimise damage if fires do occur.

TREE RETENTION

Retaining existing native vegetation plays an important role in limiting the occurrence or expansion of salting in salinity-prone catchments. Land clearing in susceptible catchments should be undertaken only with extreme caution, and only after the costs, benefits and risks of the venture have been carefully considered. Small differences in deep drainage are all that is needed to alter the hydrological cycle sufficiently to result in salting or seepage problems. Long-term and very detailed studies would be required to detect such changes.

There is little point in clearing marginally economic upland recharge areas if subsequent salinity in discharge areas takes fertile lowland areas out of production. Revegetation programs are considerably more costly than retaining the land in a naturally vegetated state. Planning for clearing in the context of a Property Management Plan will ensure that decisions will take into account all aspects of farm activities, including natural resources, finances, management implications and personal goals.

In some cases, stands of native vegetation can be used to generate a financial return in their own right. Managing stands of eucalyptus or cypress pine for commercial timber, farm timber or craft timber could provide a return at least equal to grazing if clearing, regeneration and land degradation costs are taken into account. Other enterprises based on remnant vegetation include opportunities for farm tourism, honey production and native food and seed collection.

GUIDELINES FOR RETAINING TREES

At all times, decisions to retain or clear trees based on these guidelines need to be made in conjunction with all other tree retention/clearing guidelines, legislation and limitations. There are many reasons for retaining vegetation other than for salinity control, such as biodiversity, erosion control, aesthetics, wildlife habitat, net increase or decrease in productivity of the land and so on.

Firstly, all sites that may be currently salted or that appear to have potential for developing salinity need to be investigated. These sites will be apparent on the basis of:

- any evidence of salinity at the surface
- presence of vegetation communities or species which indicate saline or wet areas
- evidence of current or periodic seepages at the soil surface or in the soil profile
- depth to watertable of less than 5 m.

Investigations at these sites should include, as a minimum:

- salinity of the groundwater
- salinity of water in drainage lines nearby
- soil profile characteristics to a depth of 2 m or to the parent rock, in particular looking for gleying, $CaCO_3$ nodules, or iron or manganese concretions or staining

Secondly, if these investigations indicate salinity, or if more comprehensive investigations are warranted on a catchment scale to identify areas with the potential to develop salinity, the search should be widened to include other areas in the catchment with similar characteristics to the sites already investigated, as well as the following areas:

- potential discharge sites of local landform types at risk of salinity
- low-lying and break-of-slope areas
- other suspect areas based on unusual soil or vegetation conditions, or areas that are prone to erosion.

If no potential discharge sites occur in the catchment, salinity risk is likely to be low, and decisions for retaining or clearing trees should comply with tree retention/clearing guidelines and limitations other than those for salinity risk.

Guidelines in addition:

- Retain a belt of trees at least 100 m wide on the toeslopes all around the catchment to help intercept increased groundwater flows and protect the valley flats from saline outbreaks.
- Retain trees along creek lines and geological contacts where permeable horizons overlie impermeable horizons.
- Retain trees along roadways and fence lines, scattered over pasture lands or incorporated into soil conservation measures in cropping lands.

Stock should be excluded from areas where vegetation has been cleared, at least periodically, to allow regeneration.

17

Engineering Methods

Engineering options such as drainage, pumping and water diversion for managing salinity and taking advantage of excess water include:

- intercepting groundwater before it reaches the discharge area, and possibly using this water, depending on quality, for irrigation or stock watering
- draining excess groundwater from discharge management areas
- diverting surface water away from discharge management areas
- evaporating saline water from evaporation basins or ring tanks.

Initial costs in implementing engineering options may appear high, but these can be balanced against potential losses from reduced land values and lost productivity and income from possible alternative uses of the water. In fact, the costs of implementing engineering options such as drainage and pumping, even during the limited period in which other controls are being established, can be considerably less than the cost of lost productivity.

Assistance with aspects of water supply, irrigation and drainage schemes is available from farm advisory services.

DRAINAGE

Drainage can be an attractive option in situations where recharge areas are not under the control of the landholder with the salinity problem and groundwater quality is good.

Extensive hydrological investigations may be required to determine whether drainage is a viable option under local conditions and to predict its likely effectiveness. When investigating drainage as a salinity management option, these factors need to be considered:

- Effective drainage requires a height difference between the watertable and the drain outlet. To drain flat or insufficiently sloping areas, pumps may be required, increasing the cost of implementation.
- The hydraulic conductivity of the soil dictates drain spacing. To be effective in clay soils, drains may need to be positioned so close together that this form of management becomes impractical. A minimum workable spacing for drains is considered to be about 80 m.
- Drainage effluent requires disposal. If the groundwater is saline, the effluent may be too salty to be released into local waterways (except possibly during times of flood). However, it may be possible to dilute the effluent with channel water for use downstream or in irrigation areas.

This can be a particularly sensitive issue in some areas where drainage water, in addition to being saline, may also carry high levels of nutrients and chemicals.

When drainage is being designed, future extensions, improvements and the drainage of adjacent areas need to be taken into account. Local extension officers (specialising in soil conservation or water resources) offer a comprehensive service for designing and installing surface and subsurface farm drainage systems.

Drainage water disposal

Any proposal to dispose of pumped or drained water requires a permit from the appropriate authority. Appropriate permits, licences, easements and so on must be arranged for any effluent disposal, regardless of the quality of the water. Outlets must be designed to prevent damage to the receiving watercourse, and the disposal of poor quality water must be managed to prevent adverse effects on other lands and water supplies.

Surface drainage

Surface drains are used to route floodwaters, subsurface drain outflows, irrigation tailwaters and any other excess surface water away from problem areas. This may reduce recharge, erosion and prolonged waterlogging and ponding, as well as providing an opportunity for reusing excess water.

Subsurface drainage

Subsurface drainage can be used to prevent waterlogging in two ways:

- Relief drainage is used where there is already a high watertable to lower the watertable below the root zone of the crop.
- Interception drainage is used to prevent waterlogging and high watertables on lower ground by intercepting seepage and transmission of groundwater from higher ground.

Many subsurface drainage systems rely on buried slotted agricultural pipe or slotted PVC pipe drains with non-slotted pipe taking the water to the discharge point. Clay pipes (tile drains) or rubble drains have also been used, but these are difficult to install and maintain. Most types of pipes tend to become blocked by plant roots after a period of time. In suitable soils, mole drains can be used to enhance flow into collector drains. Mole drains are created by dragging a 'plug' through the soil to create a tunnel for water to flow into and along to some type of outfall.

The amount and type of clay and the ESP level of the soil will determine the stability and useable life of mole drains. The quality of the drainage water will also affect the dispersibility of the soil and thus the stability of the drain.

The optimal depth for drains depends on soil type and crop. The aim is to maintain the watertable below the root zone of the crop for relief drainage, and to intercept as much seepage as possible for interception drainage.

Interception trenches

Groundwater interception trenches at right angles to the hydraulic gradient (direction of flow) can be used to intercept groundwater (Fig. 17.1). Large trenches can provide water storage and can be pumped with conventional pumping equipment. This engineering option will only be effective in areas where the groundwater can be

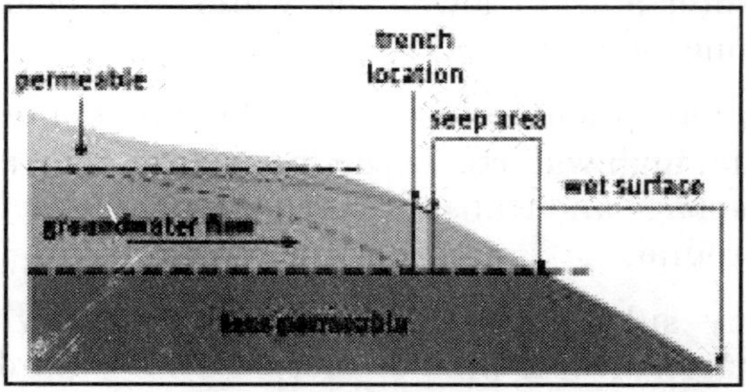

Fig. 17.1: Section through a seepage area with a trench showing the change in depth to watertable

accessed fairly close to the surface (1.5 to 5 m depth). This system is being used in the Kingaroy area Trenches which are located above breaks-of-slope, toeslopes or wetter areas upslope of some subsurface barrier to water movement will act as surface storages, being constantly recharged by the groundwater seepage.

Trenches can be pump-tested in a similar manner to bores. The volume of initial storage needs to be taken into account together with the number of trenches when determining the volume of available water. Water quality and potential uses also need to be considered before trenches are constructed.

GROUNDWATER PUMPING

To determine whether groundwater pumping is a viable option for managing salinity, the following need to be determined:

- the volume of water that needs to be pumped to reclaim the affected area
- how efficiently this volume can be extracted, method of extraction and cost
- the quality of the water to be pumped
- options for using and disposing of water of this quality, and possible benefits and consequences of its use.

The quantity of water that needs to be pumped to reclaim a waterlogged or salt-affected discharge area can be roughly estimated by calculating a groundwater balance for the catchment. The transmissivity of the aquifer and hydraulic head will determine whether the required volume can be extracted from the aquifer efficiently.

While some information can be inferred from surrounding existing bores, water quality and flow rate can only be accurately determined from a test bore in the target interception area. Flow rate will indicate which pumping options will be appropriate and economical.

Pump Site Planning

Preliminary investigations are necessary to determine the best point(s) for groundwater extraction. To select sites for preliminary investigations, the best sources of information are local knowledge, data on hydrogeology, and results of previous drilling in the area. This information will provide a guide to the likely depth to which bores will have to be sunk, and thus the likely cost of drilling. Other information that should be obtained before carrying out preliminary investigations includes whether a licence is needed to drill, the type of drill rig most suited to the job, and the means of constructing the bore(s).

Once a bore has been constructed, a pump test is useful for determining the characteristics of the aquifer at that site. This involves pumping the bore for 24 hours and measuring the change in water level over time in the bore and the volume of water being extracted at regular time intervals.

The success of a bore for groundwater extraction will depend on factors such as the extent of the aquifer, the ability of the aquifer to drain water freely, the diameter and design of the bore, and pumping interference from other bores in the vicinity. An analysis of results from preliminary investigations will determine the effect of these factors and provide an indication of the maximum capacity of the bore, optimum pump inlet level, long-term reliability of the bore and stability of the aquifer.

If the transmissivity of the groundwater aquifer is low, multiple bores may need to be installed to obtain the required quantity of water. Supplying pumps and energy sources to each of these bores would quickly make such a system uneconomical. One option is to use smaller diameter (and thus less costly) bores and manifold these together to make a single inlet for a large surface-mounted pump. However, if one bore breaks suction, the whole system will fail. Because of the limits on suction lift of a surface-mounted pump, depth to the watertable and distance between the bores will be limiting factors in this type of system. A multiple bore system is more likely to have an even drawdown of the groundwater than a single pumped bore. As a result, a multiple bore system will provide better results when the water is being extracted near to the area affected by the high watertable.

Pumps

In the case of a conventional single bore, pumping options include electric submersible pumps, electric or diesel turbines, helical rotor pumps, solar electric pumps, and windmills. Air pumps are particularly suitable for multiple bore systems.

Commercially available pumps can be categorised into three types:

- **Low flow pumps**. Generally intended for stock and domestic water movement, these pumps are designed to be very low maintenance and cost almost nothing to run. Solar pumps and windmills are in this category because these pumps do not need to be located near a conventional power source and can be left unattended for long periods. Pumping starts and stops automatically, depending on the system's energy requirements. Some domestic pumps require conventional power, but these systems are commonly located near a house where power is available. These systems generally pump up to 1 L/s, although volume throughputs in the range 0.7 to 1 L/s generally require larger, more expensive systems.
- **Low to medium flow pumps**. These are generally fire fighting type pumps for surface pumping applications with a volume throughput of 0.7 to 5

L/s. Small turbine and helical rotor pumps in this range are used for some small-scale irrigation, but as these pumps can only service a small area, they are most economical when used to irrigate highvalue crops.

- **Medium to high flow pumps**. Mostly used for largescale irrigation, these are pumps with a volume throughput greater than 5 L/s, and include diesel and electrically driven turbine and helical rotor pumps. As most of the cost of these pumps is in the drive systems and motors, their use under low to medium flow conditions is generally uneconomical.

Low to medium flow pumps with a volume throughput of approximately 0.7 to 5 L/s are appropriate for managing salinity by pumping in the transmission area. As multiple bore holes and pumping systems will probably be required to intercept a sufficient amount of water, pumps with the energy, maintenance, running and cost characteristics of low flow pumps will be most suitable.

Electric and Diesel Pumps

Electric pumping systems can be automated easily for on and off times and extended running periods. However, automated systems are limited to a single pump rate unless the pulleys are changed to vary pump speed. There can be considerable expense involved in making electricity available at the bore site if it is not already available. Tariff ratings and possible guarantees of use also need to be considered.

Diesel systems can be easily placed near to bore sites. Fuel storage will limit running times, but the pump rate can be easily changed by varying the governor setting.

Protection equipment for monitoring temperatures and pressures can easily be attached to both electric and diesel systems.

Sun- and Wind-powered Pumps

If the flow is small, solar electric pumps and windmills can be used economically. If an unused (but working) windmill is available, pumping with a windmill can be particularly economical. However, some of these systems rely on close tolerances for turbines, and pistons are susceptible to dirty, salty, sandy water; damage will result if the bore runs dry. The helical rotor pump and some solar diaphragm pumps can generally handle contaminated water without damage.

Solar-powered systems can only operate during daylight hours unless generated electricity is stored in a battery. However, it is usually cheaper to store water than electricity. As these systems are electric, it is relatively easy to install automated control and safety cut-outs. Solar powered systems are relatively portable and have a similar effective lifespan to both windmills and diesel pumps.

Air pumps

Another type of pump, not widely used in agriculture, is the air pump. These pumps can be used to provide a low-cost dewatering system for regions with low yields of 0.5 to 3 L/s.

Air pumps are particularly suitable for multiple bore systems because one compressor can be used to drive a number of bores. This is achieved by installing a network of inexpensive piping between the compressor and the water extraction points (distances can be up to several kilometres).

There are two basic types of air pumps:

- **Air injection type**. Air injected at the base of a submerged discharge pipe forms a mixture of water and air which is lighter than the head of water at this point, so the aerated water rises to the surface.

- **Pressure vessel type**. A submerged chamber is alternately filled with water and with air; when the chamber is filled with water, a control device (electronic or mechanical) directs compressed air into the chamber, which forces the water into a discharge pipe; when the chamber is empty of water, the compressed air is shut off, the vessel is allowed to refill with water, and the process repeats.

The air injection system has no moving parts in contact with water, and the pump foot piece is simple and inexpensive. The control devices used by the pressure vessel type pumps may become unreliable in the long term, and dirty water can reduce the performance of these pumps by inhibiting the action of the non-return valves. With both types, if the bore runs dry, pumping automatically resumes as the bore replenishes.

The efficiency of the air injection type is greatest when the head above the pump (that is, the depth to which the pump is submerged below the watertable) is at least 70% of the total lift required. In other words, the depth of the pump below the watertable needs to be at least 2.3 times the height difference between the watertable and the outflow point. For example, a pump situated 7 m below the watertable will lift water efficiently to 10 m. (If the watertable is lowered by pumping, the pump will need to be lowered to maintain efficiency.) Thus this system of pumping is most efficient in areas with shallow watertables where the water can be disposed of nearby using flood or furrow irrigation or held in temporary surface water storages.

18

Irrigation Management

Key issues in sustainable irrigation are:

- preventing excessive salt accumulation in the root zone
- maintaining soil structural stability
- minimising excess drainage of water below the root zone
- maintaining crop or plant productivity
- minimising off-site effects.

Whether the landholder is considering implementing irrigation or adjusting irrigation regimes, the process of investigating options is basically the same:

- Assess the quality of the water currently being used or proposed for irrigation.
- Consider characteristics of the soils in the area proposed for irrigation—in particular, soil structural stability and permeability.
- Consider characteristics of plant species proposed for the irrigated area—in particular, salt tolerance.

- Determine the likely leaching fraction of the soil and the consequent root zone salinity and amount of drainage below the root zone.
- Estimate the effects of irrigation water sodicity on soil behaviour.

Variation in the choice of crop, soil characteristics and water quality makes irrigation management decisions quite complex. The computer package SALFPREDICT is designed to consider salinity, sodicity and soil and plant factors together.

IRRIGATION MANAGEMENT TO MINIMISE WATERTABLE RISE

In irrigation areas that are supplied with surface water, efficient water management is essential to prevent watertable rise. Because some leaching below the root zone is inevitable, monitoring of water levels is an essential aspect of irrigation management. Good hydrological information is essential when planning and developing irrigation areas. When gathering and using this information, the following are important:

- Restrictions to water movement through the landscape must be identified and incorporated into plans for controlling the watertable.
- Areas with highly permeable soils (which contribute to high rates of accession to the watertable) must be identified and considered for specific irrigation management or exclusion from the irrigation scheme.

Accessions to watertables can be reduced in three ways:

- For surface water supplies with good quality water on permeable soils, more efficient water management techniques, such as trickle or microsprinkler, can be used to avoid excess water moving below the root zone. In groundwater-based systems accessing water in an unconfined aquifer, this is less of a problem, as excess drainage moves to the groundwater where it becomes available again for irrigation.

- Under flood or furrow irrigation, surface levelling promotes more uniform soil wetting on clay soils, so levelled areas can be irrigated for shorter periods for the same effect. Levelling can improve surface drainage in flat areas, assisting runoff of excess water from the soil surface.
- Selecting a water application system which is appropriate for the permeability of the particular soil is also important. With permeable soils, sprinkler or trickle irrigation is more satisfactory than flood irrigation in most cases. With heavy cracking clay soils, flood or furrow irrigation, managed to limit tail drain losses, is more efficient for wetting the soil.

In surface water schemes, seepage from supply channels can significantly contribute to watertable rises. To reduce this problem, channels can be lined (often an expensive option), or pipes or fluming can be used to distribute the water on-farm.

Subsoil drainage or watertable pumping and water reuse can be used to control high watertables. However, several factors need to be considered regarding drainage, such as whether there is an adequate height difference between the watertable and the drain outlet, soil hydraulic conductivity and its implications for drain spacing, options for disposing of drain effluent, water quality, and aquifer transmissivity.

MARGINAL QUALITY IRRIGATION WATERS

The best approach is to match soils, irrigation waters and crops to minimise negative impacts of irrigation on soils. In order to implement this, it is necessary to have an accurate assessment of water quality.

Where it is not possible to match all these factors, a number of irrigation management practices can be used to minimise the effects of marginal quality irrigation water on soils and crops. These practices include changing the frequency, duration and method of irrigation, judicious timing of leaching irrigations, mixing irrigation water supplies, and cultural practices including soil amendments. These are outlined below.

Researcher describe the limitations of several irrigation management approaches in practice. Salinity and sodicity are the two major issues with marginal quality water use. Management practices to minimise the effects of such waters are outlined in the following sections.

Saline Water

Irrigate more Frequently

Provided the root zone is wet, more frequent irrigation reduces plant water stress, dilutes the soil solution, and sometimes increases leaching of salts. Increasing irrigation frequency is appropriate where irrigation water is available on demand and soils are permeable. However, the cost of irrigation may also be increased, as may be the likelihood of watertable rise.

Use Extra Water to Control Salinity by Leaching

Two options are available here:

- In soils with good drainage and where the watertable is not high, maintain salt balance throughout the season by applying extra water each irrigation for leaching.
- Allow salt to accumulate during the growing season and then implement specific leaching irrigations (that

is, apply extra water during periodic preplanned irrigations). Water use is more efficient, but some yield loss may result from salt accumulation. In all soils other than slowly permeable soils, leaching in small amounts is more efficient than ponding. In slowly permeable soils, ponding is more efficient. Timing of leaching irrigations depends on crop salt tolerance and water salinity. For annual crops, pre- or post-crop irrigation is preferred. Pre-cropping irrigation will assist germination by leaching surface salt.

Cropping in cooler months or, alternatively, irrigating to coincide with a period of major seasonal rainfall will contribute to greater leaching. For perennial crops, leaching irrigations during dormant periods are more effective, since less evapotranspiration occurs.

With slowly permeable soils, the use of marginal quality water for leaching may contribute to higher soil salinity levels, because more salt can be added to the soil than is removed during leaching even though there is an increase in the leaching due to flocculation by the salts. In this situation, seasonal rainfall will provide leaching. In dry years, salinity effects on plants will be more severe.

Choose the Best Irrigation Method for the Conditions

The method of irrigation used can affect salt accumulation:

- Flood irrigation provides an even application of water but can be wasteful, particularly in a highfrequency irrigation scheme. In cracking clay soils, flood irrigation provides good recharge of soil water and some potential for leaching if the soil is cracked before irrigation.

- Furrow irrigation contributes to salt accumulation in adjacent rows through capillary rise and evaporation from the highest parts of the ridges. Thus planting in the furrow or on the side of larger hills will reduce salt concentration.
- Sprinkle irrigation provides good control and maximum flexibility. However, it can cause leaf damage (burn) and salt precipitation on leaves. Some water is lost through evaporation, which increases the salinity of water on the leaves. Both leaf damage and evaporation can be reduced by sprinkling at night. Precipitates on leaves can be reduced by increasing the sprinkler rotation speed. In cracking clay soils, the lower application rate of sprinkle irrigation can cause surface sealing and greatly reduce soil wetting.
- Trickle irrigation is efficient but contributes to salt accumulation in the soil surface and at the edge of wetted areas. Under rainfall, salts accumulated at the soil surface can be leached down into the root zone in sufficient concentrations to kill vegetation. These effects can be reduced by applying a surface mulch to minimise evaporation or by burying the emitter at some depth in the root zone.

Some species can tolerate higher salinity levels in the soil than in water which is applied to the leaves. This is specifically relevant to crops under irrigation. Methods for managing this situation and being able to continue to irrigate crops with marginally saline waters (in relation to each crop species) include irrigating below the leaves and irrigating at night (to reduce salt on the leaves left by rapid evaporation during the day).

Mix Water Supplies

Mixing water supplies can reduce salinity hazard if good quality water is available in addition to the marginal quality water. However, mixing a saline water with good quality water is not necessarily a good strategy. If the saline water is of higher salinity than the plant can tolerate, diluting it with a less saline water is a waste because once the threshold salinity is reached, the plant cannot use the water.

Two options are preferred for using good and marginal quality water supplies for irrigation:

- Alternate applications of marginal quality water with applications of good quality water, when available. This will maintain a lower salt balance, provided sodicity is not a problem. With species that have differing levels of salinity tolerance depending on stage of growth, water quality can be matched to stage of growth.
- Alternate salt-tolerant and salt-sensitive crops with different irrigation waters. This option is preferred where good quality water is available and seasonal rainfall promotes leaching.

Sodic Water

Sodic irrigation waters generally result in soil dispersion with consequent soil surface sealing, crusting, erosion, poor water entry and poor seedbeds. This dispersion is reduced by the salinity level in an irrigation water but problems develop under heavy rainfall when salts are leached from the soil surface. Points listed above under irrigating with marginally saline waters are generally relevant to irrigating with marginally sodic waters, in addition to the following points.

Mix Water Supplies

Mixing available waters to maintain a satisfactory sodicity level can be a viable management option, providing salinity levels are satisfactory.

Apply Gypsum

Gypsum (calcium sulfate) can be used as a soil amendment to improve the structure of surface soils and to alleviate some of the adverse effects of high sodicity waters and those with residual alkali (Na_2CO_3). Gypsum improves soil structure by increasing flocculation of clay particles through increased electrolyte concentration and by exchange of calcium for sodium on the exchange complex. This results in better surface soil aggregation and consequently reduced waterlogging and crusting and can improve surface soil drainage. Long-term benefits of gypsum in exchanging for sodium can only occur if the exchanged sodium can be leached out of the profile. Thus on soils with slowly permeable subsoils there will be limited benefits.

Gypsum has a relatively low solubility; it is estimated that no more than 700 kg of surface-applied pure gypsum can be dissolved per megalitre of irrigation water in any one year—that is, 100 mm depth of water per hectare. Thus under common conditions (assuming rainfall of 800 mm/ yr and irrigation water application of 500–600 mm/ yr), an application of around 1 t/ha/yr of pure gypsum could be dissolved. Because of impurities in gypsum, unevenness of distribution and loss from surface runoff, the general recommendation is 2–6 t/ha every year or per two-year period. In some situations, depending on the gypsum responsiveness of a soil, applications of 5 t/ha seem to be more successful in achieving a measurable effect. Gypsum added directly to irrigation water is much more effective than when applied to the soil surface, but the cost of dissolution will increase the overall cost.

Apply other Soil Amendments

Sulfur application can be useful on sodic soils if there is a high level of calcium carbonate at the soil depth required. Also, sulfuric acid can be used for high alkalinity and residual alkali waters. However, sulfuric acid is not appropriate if calcium or magnesium levels are low since sodicity will remain high. Handling this acid is dangerous.

Irrigate for Longer Periods of Time

A longer duration of irrigation is required with sodic waters since sodic soils have lower infiltration rates and need more time for the water to become wet. Irrigation across slope or recycling taildrain water will help conserve water. Long irrigations, however, can lead to aeration problems.

Choose the Best Irrigation Method for the Conditions

Spray irrigation can cause surface crusting and sealing on sodic soils if used during crop establishment without a surface mulch to protect the soil surface. Capillary wetting of hills from furrow irrigation results in less soil slaking and dispersion than spray irrigation.

Protect the Soil Surface

Medium seedbeds are preferable to fine seedbeds to reduce slaking and dispersion and crusting on irrigation. Adding large quantities of organic matter will help maintain soil structure of some soils and reduce cloddiness.

Reclaim Sodic Soils using Saline Water

If the land value is very high and there are advantages in reducing the soil sodicity levels, a reclamation method for sodic soils with very low permeability can be attempted. Using this method, high salt concentration waters are applied initially to flocculate the soil. Once the permeability is raised, the SAR of the water is gradually reduced as the salinity is reduced, resulting in low ESP and improved soil structure. This process needs to be monitored closely.

19

Evaporation Basins for Salinity Management

An evaporation basin is a means of storing saline water derived from natural or constructed drainage systems. In Western Australia, the most common form of drainage are open deep drains and groundwater pumps. In some circumstances, saline surface runoff may also require evaporation or remediation. Evaporation basins should be built as part of an integrated catchment water management plan.

Many natural salt lakes act as evaporation basins for internally drained catchments. They form part of the ephemeral river systems that store water during low flows or small rainfall events. These natural salt lakes evaporate water and accumulate salts. The lakes are periodically flushed by large rainfall runoff events. Salt is also removed from the lakes by recharge into the deeper aquifers.

WHAT IS AN EVAPORATION BASIN OR DISPOSAL BASIN?

An evaporation basin is a natural salt lake or engineered earth structure designed to impound saline water discharged from drains or groundwater pumping. The purpose of the basin is to evaporate the water and leave the crystalline salts behind. Salt is usually contained within the basin, but under certain circumstances may also be stored in groundwater beneath the basin. Evaporation basins are usually constructed downstream of drainage or pumping systems designed to protect high-value agricultural land, natural assets or built infrastructure.

Basin Design and Leakage

Basin shape and design are dependent on its purpose and the site conditions. A constructed evaporation basin can consist of a single basin or a number of basins (cells). In a multiple-cell system, the saline water from the first cell is partially evaporated to increase the salt concentration. The water is then transferred to the next cell for further evaporation and concentration. In the final cell, the crystallised salt can be harvested.

Sealed Basins

Sealed evaporation basins have a clay or plastic liner installed to prevent saline water leaking from the basin. Installing a liner significantly increases the cost of construction.

Sealed basins are used where:

- the risk of significant leakage is high;
- the groundwater beneath the basin has the potential to become polluted from leakage; and
- there is a risk to downstream assets from leakage.

Liners are often required when salt harvesting is proposed.

Leaky Basins

Controlled leakage of concentrated saline water maintains the optimum salt concentration and evaporation rate in the basin. Most evaporation basins in eastern Australia are designed to leak at an accepted rate.

Leakage rates of greater than 3 mm/d are undesirable as evaporation efficiency is reduced and recovery of the leakage at these rates may become unmanageable. In designing a basin, the physical plan must ensure that leakage is forecast, managed and that suitable recovery systems are in place. Drains and pumps can be used to capture most if not all of the basin leakage.

Where natural lakes are used as an evaporation basin, an assessment of the lakes' natural hydrology and leakage is required. Flood stripping (salt removed by large floods) from the lake system may be possible to allow for salts to be discharged from the lake at a time when there is sufficient water flow to dilute the saline discharge.

WHY USE AN EVAPORATION BASIN?

The drainage and pumping of saline water requires a safe disposal point. In some cases natural channels and streams can be used, but where no other feasible disposal option is available, evaporation basins must be used to receive the discharge. Note that a Notice of Intent to Drain (NOID) must be submitted before discharging water from drains or pumps.

In the Murray–Darling drainage system, there are approximately 120 'constructed' evaporation basins in use today with a total area that exceeds 16,000 ha. These basins dispose of up to 210 GL/yr of saline water (1 Gigalitre (GL) is equivalent to 1,000 Megalitres (ML) or 1 metre of water on 100 ha). These small to large community-scale salt disposal basins are used to impound saline water from tile drainage and pumping systems installed to protect farmland. Similar systems can be installed in Western Australia where effective rates of extraction or drainability of soils is proven.

Some basins are used for aquaculture production, such as brine shrimp, fish, alga and the commercial harvesting of salts. This farmnote does not consider such specialist uses of basins as each is complex and requires individual designs.

WHERE TO INSTALL AN EVAPORATION BASIN?

For an evaporation basin to be effective and have minimum leakage, it should be constructed:

- in soils with low permeability;
- in flat areas (with little watertable slope);
- in areas with shallow groundwater;
- in soils that allow recovery of leakage;
- away from the influence of flood events (unless designed to be stripped);
- where there is high groundwater salinity (so basin leakage will have limited impact on the groundwater quality);
- away from built infrastructure (which may be at risk from leakage and to avoid problems associated with visual pollution and odours); and
- where there is adequate space available for expansion of the structure to occur if inflows are exceeded.

PLANNING AN EVAPORATION BASIN

All evaporation basins must be designed to strict engineering and environmental standards. The legal and community approval requirements must be fulfilled and the level of community consultation should reflect the scale and risk from each basin.

It is highly recommended that groups considering constructing an evaporation basin seek engineering design and related support from qualified contractors.

The primary steps in planning for an evaporation basin are to:

- determine the inflow from all sources (drain flow, runoff, direct rainfall);
- determine the basin area;
- determine the chemistry of runoff water, specifically pH, and ion chemistry
- assess the physical and chemical conditions of the soil;
- assess the environmental and social impact of the basin;
- develop a 'lifetime' management plan for the basin; and
- ensure legal approval and community consultation has occurred.

Calculating Inflow and Basin Area

Basin design, cost and operation depend on

- accurately estimating the daily inflow to the basin
- the relationship between the evaporative area, water salinity and depth.

Inflow calculations should include estimates of average daily drain discharge (kilolitres per day), taking account of variations due to higher initial flows following drain construction, storm flows (inflow of run-off) and direct precipitation (for example, using 1:10-year average recurrence intervals). The ease of estimation of inflow will be dependant on drain design. For example inflows derived from pumping systems or leveed drains will be easier to estimate than those that are drains that allow the entry of surface runoff.

Calculations must include known variations in inflow salt concentra-tion. The variation in salt concentration may effect long-term evaporation capacity and therefore size of the basin. As a result of high salinity levels in the Western Australian wheatbelt groundwater, basins operating in the wheatbelt may only evaporate at approximately 50–75% of net pan evaporation rates. This is because evaporation rates are reduced when the salinity of the water is increased. Basins should be designed to be of sufficient size to enable evaporation of annual inflow, but not be of a size to allow the basin to completely dry. Basin layout (multiple cells, several evaporators and crystalliser) and size will also be dependent on the basin water balance and salt-harvesting options.

SOIL ASSESSMENT

Site tests should include the full range of soil-related engineering tests, in particular, those related to conditions of the soil when saline water and compaction have modified it. Soil tests should be conducted at a scale comparable with the soil variability, with greater numbers of deep-soil pits being dug in less uniform areas.

Tests should also be conducted to determine the effect of wave action on the basin walls and the effect of soil compaction by machinery and related monitoring infrastructure needs to be considered. Clay and plastic liners are generally not used because of the cost. Soil behaviour in the presence of high salt loads should be evaluated.

Aquifer tests are required. Deep soil profiles should be assessed, taking note of soil structure and texture, variations in permeability (especially in the upper 5 m), watertable elevation, groundwater chemistry and whether the groundwater level is stable or rising over time.

In a study of evaporation basins in the Murray-Darling Basin, only once did the permeability of the basin floor determine the final leakage rate. At all other sites, it was the aquifer (deep soil) permeability and the capacity of the aquifer to transmit water away from the basin that controlled the leakage rate. The influences on aquifer permeability are likely to be similar that of the MDBC. In particular the effect of basin leakage is likely to occur close to the basin due to low permeability and gradient that dominate wheatbelt sites.

ENVIRONMENTAL AND SOCIAL IMPACT

An engineering-based risk assessment should be undertaken on all potential sites. The level of assessment should increase as the potential risks to the environment and community increases. The impact of design failure should also be considered.

As all unsealed evaporation basins have a tendency to leak, they should be monitored and designed to allow for groundwater recovery. Deep drains located around the perimeter of the basin and tube wells down-gradient can be used to manage and monitor leakage before it has a major impact. This water can then be pumped back into the basin.

For natural disposal basins (modified salt lakes), flood stripping (salt washed away by large floods) has been proposed as a means of providing a greater lifespan for the basin. An environmental impact assessment on this form of basin design should be completed in detail before use. Criteria for the design of such basins must be based on detailed hydrology and downstream river hydrodynamics. In Western Australia this may be dependent on the seasonal variation of flow, given that a large proportion of creek and river systems are ephemeral.

BASIN MANAGEMENT PLANS

A basin management plan needs to stipulate the methods of operating the basin over long periods. Clear design standards and implementation guidelines need to be in place. Design criteria indicate basins should be designed for a minimum of 50 years. Factors to be considered include inflow (the amount of water, sediment, salt), salt movement within the basin, harvesting and salt removal, leakage, bank stability, basin failure and others such as odours, access, waterbird usage, monitoring and aesthetics. Basin owners and managers are responsible for the consequences of their design and NOIDs are required to be lodged at least 90 days before discharge via drains or pumping can commence.

Basin owners, with support from local government and related regulatory bodies are required to undertake and develop:

- planning and approval processes;
- monitoring requirements;
- risk assessment;
- contingency procedures, decommissioning requirements; and
- a statement of accountability.

20

Saline Seeps Management with Siphons

Locally known as "alkali spots" or "slick spots," they are areas of bare soil or reduced crop production, usually located on a side-hill, a toe-slope, or low-lying area. Seeps range in size from a few square yards to tens of acres. They tend to stay wet longer than surrounding areas, and may discharge water during wet periods. During dry periods, white salt crystals may be visible on the surface.

Seeps reduce land value in many ways, including loss of crop production, inconvenience, loss or inefficient use of inputs, and erosion. Seeps usually occur on what would otherwise be very productive soil. The scattered nature of seeps makes it inconvenient to "farm around them," yet it is often impossible to cross them with field machines. If you have noticed some of the initial signs of seep development (wet areas, often having very good crop production), you may want to take steps to control the seep before it develops into a barren area.

If crops or range plants do not use all the water that enters the soil, the excess water moves downward. In many soils, this downward movement tends to slow as the water encounters zones of slow permeability or compacted layers. When this happens, water moves laterally until it approaches the soil surface. Once the water is within 2 to 3 feet of the soil's surface, capillary action can lift the water to the surface, where it evaporates and leaves salts behind.

In a semiarid climate like central Kansas, it is difficult to believe that seeps are caused by excess water. You can verify this by digging a posthole (3 to 4 feet deep) in an established seep. You will probably bring up saturated soil, and if you return after 24 hours, you are likely to find water standing in the bottom of the hole. Dryland seeps are common in areas having much less rainfall than Kansas.

GROUNDWATER SIPHON DESCRIPTION

A groundwater siphon is a fully primed pipe inserted into a bore or deep pit that acts like a passive vacuum pump. Provided the outlet of the pipeline is at a lower elevation than the water level in the bore, groundwater will move in the direction of the outlet because it is at a lower (hydraulic) pressure. In practice, and given the right conditions, siphons can lower watertables to about 8.3 m (note the theoretical limit is 10.2 m).

Water levels beneath saline seeps will be lowered significantly if the flow from the siphon (or multiple siphons) is greater than the flow of groundwater to the site. A siphon is constructed using a vertical pipe, which extends down the inside of the bore and a horizontal pipe (of the same diameter) that extends along the surface. A simple elbow-pipe joiner is used to connect the two pipes. The vertical pipe should be designed to reach the bottom of the borehole, reduce the potential for silt accumulation in the bore and to ensure the maximum possible drawdown. When a groundwater siphon is activated, the water level within the bore falls and friction within the pipeline increases. As a result of this friction the outlet of the pipe needs to be significantly lower than the original bore water level and below the level to which the watertable is to be lowered.

BORE CONSTRUCTION

Given the geological nature of most hillside seepage areas within south Western Australia, bores normally comprise of a drilled diameter of approximately 100 mm, allowing the insertion of a 50 mm diameter PVC pipe. The average depth of siphon bores was found to be 25 metres. Commercially available perforated well screen and gravel pack should be inserted in the lower 6 m of the bore. In places where aquifers are thicker, longer well screens and more gravel pack is recommended. All wells must be developed before inserting the siphon pipe.

Selecting the Correct Siphon Pipe Diameter

To prevent dissolved gas causing the siphon to fail, siphons must either be equipped with mechanical purging devices (expensive and high maintenance) or the siphon flow and velocity should be matched to the pipe size, so that gas bubbles are ejected from the pipeline as they are created. The so-called 'critical flow rate' of groundwater siphons must be estimated and is mainly dependent on the diameter of the horizontal pipeline. For siphons to work, the pipeline must be sufficiently long (to draw maximum flow rates of water from the bore) and sufficiently small in diameter (to ensure high water speed).

What is the Minimum Gradient or Slope for a Siphon to Operate?

The minimum gradient for a siphon to operate is dependent on the pipe diameter. Small diameter pipes require lower gradients than large diameter pipes. Flow is also dependent on the operating water level and the permeability of the material from which water is extracted. Bores with flow > 0.2 L/s and with a high operating water level require lower gradients to be effective. As an approximation, most groundwater siphons (less than 35 mm in diameter) require a gradient > 1.5%. Other sites and conditions may require gradients > 2.0%.

Impact on Saline Areas

Based on research work and an evaluation of the trial sites during 2000 to 2002, the impact of siphons was determined. The impact at the various sites evaluated suggested that:

- the radial distance impacted by the siphons ranged from 50-130 m and was site-dependent;
- watertables were lowered by at least 2 m (or more) within 18 months;
- maintenance of the flow was important in de-watering a site due to the rapid rise of watertables after siphons ceased to flow;
- site selection was determined by geological and topographical parameters;
- single siphons were effective in small areas, with a multiple system used for larger areas;
- reclamation of the site is dependent on the ability of accumulated salts to leach down the soil profile;
- deep-ripping and other soil amelioration techniques (i.e. gypsum) is required to enhance the rate of salt leaching and land productivity recovery; and
- the high degree in the spatial variability of hydraulic conductivity and low permeability restrict the areal impact of the siphons as a control measure.

Issues with Siphons

Groundwater siphons may be an effective method of reducing water levels in saline areas and generating reliable supplies of water for stock and aquaculture related uses. To improve the productivity of soils after water levels have been lowered, salt levels must be reduced in the topsoil and soil organic matter and nutrient levels re-established.

All engineering systems, which involve the transfer of groundwater to the surface and local streamlines, require notification and assessment. A Notice of Intent (NOI) to drain must be submitted to the Commissioner of Soil and Land Conservation 90 days prior to commencing works.

21

Salinity Problems of the Dryland Regions and Water Quality and Crop Production

Apart from irrigated areas, salinity poses a major management problem in many unirrigated areas where cropping is done under rainfed conditions. Dryland salinity has been a threat to the land and water resources in several parts of the world although only in recent years has the seriousness of the problem become widely known. Dryland salinity is an acute management problem. Dryland salinity is also said to occur in South Africa, Iran, Afghanistan, Thailand and India and it probably exists in other countries. Saline spots or areas occurring in the dryland fields have been known by several local names, but most commonly as saline seeps. These problem soils range from a slightly saline soil condition which reduces crop growth to extensive areas where cultivation is almost impossible. Problems relating to the origin and management of dryland saline soils have been discussed at several meetings in the recent past.

MODE OF FORMATION

Dryland saline seepage is generally considered to be a manifestation of salt accumulation in seepage spots at low points or side slopes in the landscape developed when water infiltrates into soil to somewhat impermeable layers, and moves laterally downslope. Eventually at lower elevations, the water seeps laterally out at the soil surface and evaporates leaving the salts behind. Thus the development of saline seeps involves two areas in the field - the recharge and the discharge areas. In the recharge areas, water in excess of the retention capacity of the root zone soil percolates beyond the root zone, reaches the groundwater and increases the flow to the discharge area. The groundwater flow is mainly lateral and downslope and occurs most often over a shallow, less permeable layer. The groundwater travelling to the discharge area dissolves salts from the soil. In the discharge area the groundwater rises to the soil surface creating a seep. As the water evaporates from the seepage area salts accumulate.

FACTORS INFLUENCING FORMATION OF SALINE SEEPS

A combination of climatic, geologic, soil and cultural conditions determines the nature, extent and intensity of saline seeps.

Excess Water

Many dryland areas which are now cropped, existed under forest or grass cover. The ecosystem under these conditions was balanced - the grasses and trees utilizing all the precipitation in their respective areas and keeping the groundwater tables low. Clearing deep rooted perennial vegetation and its replacement by pastoral species and crops decreased plant water requirements, causing a surplus exceeding the retention capacity of the root zone. Any land use practice which allows excess moisture to migrate downward through the soil profile beneath the root zone can contribute to the formation and extension of dryland salinity. Some of the more important factors and practices that encourage excess moisture are:

- i. **Fallowing:** By far the most important contributing factor in many areas, e.g. Northern Plains of North America is the widespread alternate crop-fallow farming system. When fallowing is practised, the capacity of the soil to retain rain water is reduced resulting in greater losses through seepage.

ii. **Rainfall:** It has generally been observed that salinity problems are more severe in years of high rainfall due to greater recharge and therefore accumulation of salt-laden water in the recharge zone.

iii. **Water and snow accumulation:** Practices which result in the accumulation of water/snow in the recharge areas may aggravate the saline seep problem. These include shelter belts, single row wind breaks, railways, roads and highways, etc. Natural and constructed ponds, dugouts and small farm reservoirs can be important locally if they are located in the recharge areas and leak significant quantities of water.

iv. **Overgrazing:** Range that is overgrazed utilizes and holds in place less moisture than before resulting in increased runoff and deep percolation.

Soil Characteristics

Light textured soils having low moisture retention and high permeability in the recharge zone are more conducive to the formation of saline seeps at low points in the landscape. In some places the bed rock is of marine origin and its overburden is rich in soluble salts. Dissolution of this salt and its transportation with percolating water causes serious salinity problems. In many areas having saline seep problems the bed rock or the overburden are not of marine origin but the salts are derived from the normal weathering of the mineral constituents of the soil. Excess salts are rarely a problem in the place of their origin.

PREVENTION AND MANAGEMENT OF SALINE SEEPS

Since the cause of saline seeps is nearly always increased recharge in an upper area, any long-term solutions to the problem must include regional land use changes with the objective of at least partly restoring the original hydrological state. Apart from measures to restore the hydrologic equilibrium, site specific treatments of salt-affected land are required to restore their productivity. Since the problem is invariably complex, it is essential to devise an effective strategy for each region involving both regional land use changes and site treatment. For such strategies detailed investigations of the processes, sources and movement of salts must be worked out. Some of the more frequently recommended practices are discussed below.

Practices for the Recharge Area

Any practices that will increase water use in the recharge areas or in other ways decrease the excess water which ultimately contributes to the seepage will help in the control of saline seeps.

i. **Intensive cropping:** Intensive cropping and elimination of long fallows result in increased water use in the recharge area, decreased seepage flow and therefore a reduced salinity problem.

ii. **Growing deep rooted perennials:** Crops differ significantly in their rooting depth and seasonal water use. Research in Montana showed that among the crops tested, alfalfa had the deepest rooting system (6.10 m) and depleted the maximum soil water (787 mm). These scientists studied the effect of six years of cropping with alfalfa on a saline seep recharge discharge area. In 1971, the watertable depth was 0.30 m below the soil surface in the discharge area and at 6.2 m in the recharge area. Six years later the watertable dropped by 2.9 m in the discharge area and by 2.0 m in the recharge area. Research is also underway to test several other crops and cropping sequences in relation to control of saline seeps.

iii. **Drainage:** Surface drainage of natural and man-made ponds in the recharge area is an effective, important and often inexpensive method of controlling excess water in the seepage areas. Drainage of ponded water in the recharge area should be preferred over drainage measures in the seep area. In the latter, additional problems are encountered which include disposal of saline effluents, lack of adequate outlets, etc. While surface drainage may be adequate for removing excess water from the recharge areas, it is often necessary to resort to subsurface drainage in the discharge areas which is a costly proposition.

Practices for the discharge areas

i. **Cropping:** As in the case of recharge areas, intensive cropping involving perennial and deep rooted crops having a high water use helps in maintaining the watertable at greater depths and checks salinization.

ii. **Drainage:** The objective of drainage in the discharge areas is to lower the watertable and desalinize the root zone through leaching. Artificial subsurface drainage and leaching by applied water are generally not economic in the dryland areas. Even so, drainage works have been installed with variable performance in limited areas. Reserarchers experimented with mole drains which are made by pulling a bullet shaped object through the soil with a mole plough. It consists primarily of a beam with a perpendicular blade extending downwards. On the end of the blade is the bullet shaped object which leaves a channel. The drains are quickly installed and the installation cost is low. Mole drains perform best in soils with sufficient clay content to be cohesive and where the soil is wet enough to be plastic. The disadvantages of the mole drains are the limited depth (60 to 70 cm) to which these can be made and their relatively short life span (2 to 3 years).

According to researchers subsurface drainage of most saline seep discharge areas is unfeasible because of extremely low permeability of soils resulting from high content of montmorillonite clay and often high SAR of the soil solution, problems of waste disposal, poor accessibility for heavy drainage equipment and difficulty in locating saline seep focal points. Also the cost of materials and installation is relatively high and is often more than the land price. From these considerations, it would be better to provide drainage and adopt excess water control measures in the recharge area rather than to control the watertable through drainage in the discharge areas.

iii. **Salt-tolerant crops:** Planting salt-tolerant species is an effective way of obtaining some economic returns while efforts are being made to improve the saline seeps. Investigations on the relative tolerance of plant species in several Australian states have indicated the value of growing the following in the saline seep areas:

Agropyron elongatum	*Puccinellia ciliata*
Atriplex spp.	*Sporobolus virginicus*
Hordeum hystrix	*Trifolium fragiferum;*

Kochia brevifolia	*T. glomeratum*
Lolium rigidum	*T. resupinatum*
Paspalum vaginatum	*T. subterranum*

WATER QUALITY AND CROP PRODUCTION

Crop production in the arid and semi-arid regions is dependent on irrigated agriculture. The hot and dry climates of these regions require that the irrigation water does not contain soluble salts in amounts that are harmful to the plants or have an adverse effect on the soil properties. Water of such quality is usually not available in sufficient quantities to satisfy the water requirements of all the crops grown. Under these conditions the farmers are obliged to use irrigation water with high quantities of dissolved salts, invariably accompanied by yield reductions of most crops. Indiscriminate use of such water can often lead to crop failures and to the development of saline or sodic soils which, in turn, require expensive treatment to make them productive again. On the other hand, when saline water is skilfully used, it can contribute to the successful production of a variety of crops.

The original source of salts in irrigation water is the rock that forms a part of the earth's crust - it is constantly subject to weathering which releases salts to be carried away by water. When the soil becomes truly saline, the visible surface evidence might be a white crust or dark, moist, oily looking patch. However, salt accumulation begins to affect crop yields long before visible signs of its presence appear.

Hazards Associated with Water Quality

There are three principal problems that can arise from the quality of irrigation water delivered to the agricultural fields.

Salinity Hazard

This is directly related to the quantity of salts dissolved in the irrigation water. All irrigation water contains potentially injurious salts and nearly all the dissolved salts are left in the soil after the applied water is lost by evaporation from the soil or through transpiration by the plants. Unless the salts are leached from the root zone, sooner or later they will accumulate in quantities which will partially or entirely prevent growth of most crops.

Sodicity (Alkali) Hazard

This is another problem often confronting long-term use of certain water for irrigation and relates to the maintenance of adequate soil permeability so that the water can infiltrate and move freely through the soil. The problem develops when irrigation water contains relatively more sodium ions than divalent calcium and magnesium ions while the total concentration of salts is generally not very high. Accumulation of sodium ions on to the exchange complex results in a breakdown of soil aggregates responsible for good soil structure needed for free movement of water and air through the soils. As in the case of sodic soils, accumulation of sodium on the exchange complex can be reduced by applying appropriate quantities of amendments, e.g. gypsum.

Toxicity Hazard

A third problem results from the existence, in some water, of such toxic substances as boron or heavy metals. Boron, though an essential element for plant growth and nutrition, is required only in very small amounts. A high concentration of boron in the irrigation water can have a toxic effect on the growth of many plants. Similarly, certain other ions, e.g. chloride, sodium, etc., could prove toxic to specific crops if present in excessive quantities.

There are other factors which could influence the suitability of water for irrigation but one or more of the above factors are of concern in most situations and are discussed below.

Salinity Problems

A salinity problem related to water quality occurs if the total quantity of salts in the irrigation water is such that the salts accumulate in the root zone to the extent that crop yields are adversely affected. The salinity level of an irrigation water can be determined directly by evaporation of a known quantity of water and measuring the residue of dissolved salts that remain. The results are often expressed in parts of salt per million parts of water (mg/l). An indirect and a more common method of determining the salt content of an irrigation water is to measure its electrical conductivity (EC). The greater the conductivity, the greater is its salt content. EC of irrigation water is expressed in deci Siemens per metre at 25 °C (dS/m), superseding the old millimhos per centimetre (mmho/cm). Irrigation water has a wide range of total salinity. Most surface irrigation water, whose source is snow-fed rivers, has a total salinity of less than about 0.5 to 0.6 dS/m. Groundwater in the semi-arid and arid regions has generally higher salinity and may vary from less than one dS/m to more than 12 to 15 dS/m. Sea water is highly saline with an average total soluble salts content of about 35 g/l corresponding to an electrical conductivity of about 50 dS/m. The higher the total salinity of an irrigation water, the higher is its salinity hazard for the crops if the soil and climatic conditions and the cultural practices remain the same.

Soil, crop, climatic and cultural factors which promote accumulation of soluble salts in the root zone are inimical to the utilization of high salinity water for irrigation. Similarly, factors that promote leaching of salts from the root zone through periodic leaching favour the utilization of high salinity water for irrigation. Under favourable conditions groundwater with salinity of more than 10 dS/m has been used for the production of semi-tolerant crops like wheat in coarse textured soils with only slight yield reductions. On the other hand unfavourable soil and climatic conditions and/or poor management have resulted in serious salinity problems even with the use of water of as low salinity as 0.4 to 0.5 dS/m. Researchers reviewed the existing information on the subject and developed practical guidelines for evaluating water quality for irrigation. In arriving at these guidelines the authors made certain basic assumptions which must be kept in view while evaluating any irrigation water for its suitability. These assumptions are:

- **Yield Potential:** Full production capability of all crops, without the use of special practices, is assumed when the guidelines indicate no restrictions on use. A 'restriction on use' indicates that there may be a limitation in choice of crop, or special management may be needed to maintain full production capability. A 'restriction on use' does not indicate that the water is unsuitable for use.

- **Site Conditions:** Soil texture ranges from sandy loam to clay loam with good internal drainage. There is no uncontrolled shallow water table present within 2 metres of the surface. The climate is semi-arid to arid and rainfall is low. Rainfall does not play a significant role in meeting crop water demand or leaching requirement. (However, in a monsoon climate or in areas where precipitation is high for part or all of the year, infiltrated water from rainfall is effective in meeting all or part of the leaching requirement; in these cases, the restrictions are less severe.)

- **Methods and Timing of Irrigations**: Normal surface or sprinkler irrigation methods are used.

Water is applied infrequently, as needed, and the crop utilizes a considerable portion of the available stored soil-water (50 per cent or more) before the next irrigation. At least 15 per cent of the applied water percolates below the root zone (leaching fraction [LF] ^{3}15 per cent). The guidelines are too restrictive for specialized irrigation methods, such as localized drip irrigation, which results in near daily or frequent irrigations, but are applicable for subsurface irrigation if surface applied leaching satisfies the leaching requirements.

- **Water Uptake by Crops**: Different crops have different water uptake patterns, but all take water from wherever it is most readily available within the rooting depth. On average about 40 per cent is assumed to be taken from the upper quarter of the rooting depth, 30 per cent from the second quarter, 20 per cent from the third quarter, and 10 per cent from the lowest quarter. Each irrigation leaches the upper root zone and maintains it at a relatively low salinity. Salinity increases with depth and is greatest in the lower part of the root zone. The average salinity of the soil-water is three times that of the applied water and is representative of the average root zone salinity to which the crop responds. These conditions result from a leaching fraction of 15-20 per cent and irrigations that are timed to keep the crop adequately watered at all times.

Salts leached from the upper root zone accumulate to some extent in the lower part but a salt balance is achieved as salts are moved below the root zone by sufficient leaching. The higher salinity in the lower root zone becomes less important if adequate moisture is maintained in the upper, 'more active' part of the root zone and long-term leaching is accomplished.

- **Restriction on Use**: The 'Restriction on Use' is divided into three degrees of severity: none, slight to moderate, and severe. The divisions are somewhat arbitrary since change occurs gradually and there is no clear-cut breaking point. A change of 10 to 20 per cent above or below a guideline value has little significance if considered in proper perspective with other factors affecting yield. Field studies, research trials and observations have led to these divisions, but management skill of the water user can alter them. Values shown are applicable under normal field conditions prevailing in most irrigated areas in the arid and semi-arid regions of the world.

On the other hand, if water is used which exceeds the values shown for the 'severe' restriction on use, the user will probably experience soil or cropping problems. With water quality values between these guides, a gradually increasing restriction on use is likely to be experienced as the water quality deteriorates. Specific conditions that may warrant a modification in the suggested values include the leaching fraction, the conditions of drainage, method of irrigation, the climate including rainfall, physical soil conditions, tolerance of crops shown to salinity and the chemical soil characteristics.

Management Practices for Efficient Use of High Salinity Water

It would thus seem that there can be very wide variations in the permissible limits of salinity levels of water for irrigation. For this reason any rigid generalizations may prove disadvantageous for field level workers and there is need to develop guidelines for each major area having similar soil, climatic and agricultural conditions. More important however is our ability to use a water of a particular salinity level under a given set of conditions. Management practices can often be modified to obtain a more favourable distribution of salts in the profile and therefore better crop yields, water quality remaining the same. Management practices that can help to overcome a high salinity problem of the irrigation water are discussed below. Desalinization of water to remove soluble salts has often been referred to as a technical possibility but at the present stage of available technologies it is doubtful if this method can have any large-scale application in the utilization of saline water for irrigation of most agricultural crops, at least in the near future.

More Frequent Irrigation

The adverse effects of the high salinity of irrigation water on the crops can be minimized by irrigating them frequently. More frequent irrigations maintain higher soil water contents in the upper parts of the root zone while reducing the concentration of soluble salts. Both these factors result in reduced effect of high salts on the availability of water to plants and therefore promote better crop growth. The sprinkler method of irrigation is generally more amenable to increased frequency of water applications. In surface irrigation methods however, more frequent irrigations almost invariably result in an appreciable increase in water use.

Selection of Salt Tolerant Crops and Varieties

As indicated in previous sections, there is a wide range in the relative tolerance of agricultural crops to soil salinity. Proper choice of crops can result in good returns even when using high salinity water, whereas use of such water for growing a relatively salt-sensitive crop may be questionable. Similarly, selection and breeding of salt-resistant crop varieties offer tremendous possibilities of utilizing saline water resources for crop production. Some workers have suggested induction of salt tolerance by soaking seeds for a certain period in salt solutions as a method for obtaining increased yields in saline water irrigated soils, while others suggest that growing seeds obtained from parents that have been irrigated with saline water helps in obtaining higher crop yields. These suggestions, however, have not been tested extensively on a field scale.

Conjunctive Use of Fresh and Saline Waters

There are situations where good quality water is available for irrigation but not in adequate quantities to meet the evapotranspirational needs of crops. Under these conditions, the strategies for obtaining maximum crop production could include mixing of high salinity water with good quality water to obtain irrigation water of medium salinity for use throughout the cropping season. Alternatively, good quality water could be used for irrigation at the more critical stages of growth, e.g. germination, and the saline water at the stages where the crop has relatively more tolerance. Further research is needed to define the best options considering the tolerance of crops at different growth stages, critical stages of growth vis-a-vis soil salinity, etc.

Cultural Practices

Cultural practices can often be modified to reduce the hazard of high salts in the irrigation water. Similarly a modification in the method of irrigation can result in improved use of water for some crops. These aspects have been discussed earlier.

The Toxicity Problem

Apart from the salinity or the sodicity hazard, the constituents of much irrigation water may cause toxicity problems when taken up by the plants in excess amounts. The toxic constituents of major concern are sodium, chloride and boron. Fruit trees, vines and woody ornamentals are especially sensitive to sodium and chloride ions. Most annual crops are not so sensitive but may be affected by higher concentrations. Sodium and chloride ions are freely taken up by the plants and become concentrated as water is lost through transpiration. Toxicity results when the concentration of these elements exceeds the tolerance limits of the plants. 'Leaf burn' scorch, and dead tissue along the outside edges of leaves are typical symptoms of sodium toxicity which first occur in the oldest leaves, usually appearing as a burn or drying of tissue at the outer edges of the leaf. As the severity increases, the drying progresses towards the leaf centre until the entire tissue is dead. Injury due to chloride toxicity however, typically, starts at the extreme leaf tip of older leaves and progresses from the tip back as the severity increases.

A slight excess of boron in the irrigation water or in the soil solution can cause toxicity to a variety of crops. Boron is taken up by the crop and is accumulated. For example, as little as 0.6 mg elemental boron per litre in the irrigation water may produce toxicity symptoms in citrus leaves; 1 mg/l may reduce the yields of citrus and certain stone fruits and 4 mg/l is harmful to many crops.

Other constituents of some irrigation water, such as lithium, selenium, molybdenum, fluoride and chromium may have deleterious effects on plants or animals even at very low concentration; however their occurrence in irrigation water has only very occasionally been reported.

Management Practices

Field practices that can eliminate or reduce the hazard due to presence of toxic elements include irrigating the crops more frequently. Frequent irrigations reduce the effective concentration of toxic constituents and therefore their adverse effect. Occasional application of excess water to leach the salts will further reduce the amounts of toxic elements in the root zone. Accumulation of sodium in plant parts can usually be reduced by maintaining a favourable concentration of calcium ions in the soil solution. Adequate quantities of calcium in the irrigation water and soil solution prevent excessive uptake of sodium by plants. Application of amendments, such as soluble calcium salts or sulphuric acid, can therefore greatly reduce the toxicity hazard due to excess sodium. Blending of water supplies, planting less sensitive crops, improving drainage conditions through profile modification, use of fertilizers in optimum doses to obtain otherwise vigorously growing plants etc. are some of the other practices that will help overcome toxicity problems.

22

Managing Soil Salinity to Boost Food Security

The build-up of salts in soil (salinization) affects agricultural land right across the world, but is most acute in dry areas. Crop growth and yield are poor. This impacts badly on farmers, reducing incomes or even forcing them off the land. Salinization is a particular problem in irrigated agriculture, reducing the world's irrigated area by 1–2% each year.

Tackling the effect of salinization in agriculture is crucial for achieving food security. But in many affected countries, clear strategies for reducing or managing salinity in agriculture and investing in addressing the problem are limited. Through its country partnerships with agricultural ministries and research agencies in Central Asia, Egypt, Iraq, and Iran, ICARDA is developing research-based coping strategies for farmers and water managers dealing with salinization. This experience, the practices developed with partners, and research can benefit other areas of the world where agricultural production is threatened by increasing levels of salinity, such as China, Pakistan, India, and other countries.

During 2012, ICARDA worked with farmers and water managers in regions affected by soil salinization to develop and implement science-based techniques for improving agriculture. The Center also used remote sensing and field surveying to create salinity maps: an invaluable resource in establishing where to concentrate resources.

The expertise and guidance provided by ICARDA offer a springboard to partner countries. With ICARDA's support, several of these nations are now in a position to continue activities towards the development of national strategies for managing salinity and improving food security.

TARGETING AFFECTED REGIONS

In Egypt's Nile Delta, ICARDA studied salinity problems in irrigation water, caused by the shallow groundwater associated with the delta's flat terrain. The research also considered how artificial surface and sub-surface drainage systems contribute to improved salinity management. Actively managing drainage systems, as opposed to the more traditional passive drainage systems, allows for more efficient water use while optimizing salt leaching from the soil.

In West Asia, ICARDA's research and development targeted the Mesopotamian plain in Iraq and the Lower Karkheh Basin in Iran. In the former, water availability is limited, irrigation water is affected by salinity in the plain between the Tigris and Euphrates rivers, and millennia of irrigation practices have led to a widespread accumulation of salts in the soil and groundwater. In the latter, insufficient natural drainage and increasing water shortages have led to the salinization of agricultural land.

Improved irrigation management at the farm level reduces water seepage into groundwater, thus reducing the processes contributing to increased salinity. In the Mesopotamian plain, the introduction and development of a salinity management framework for a regional approach to salinity management was the main output of the project.

In Central Asia, ICARDA considered how the expansion of irrigated areas has reduced water resources overall and created a build-up of salts in the soil. In particular, ICARDA studied methods to manage soil salinity under different climate change scenarios, using increased drought and salt-tolerant wheat varieties and improved water and soil management practices.

TAKING A TWO-FOLD APPROACH

Scientists at ICARDA follow two main strategies for managing soil salinization: fighting salinity and living with salinity. Fighting salinity involves reducing the impact of salinity on potentially productive lands. One way to do this is to reclaim or install drainage systems that allow salts to be washed out of the soil in combination with better irrigation water management, creating salinity levels acceptable to productive crops. The national agricultural research organizations partnering with ICARDA in West and Central Asia and the Nile Delta are applying improved management systems.

Living with salinity is a more pragmatic approach whereby ICARDA looks at ways of adapting to more saline conditions. For example, during 2012, ICARDA worked with national agricultural research partners on improving wheat varieties in Uzbekistan. Another activity involved a socioeconomic study in the southern part of Iraq to investigate alternative income sources to salinized agriculture.

23

Glossary

Alkali soil - A soil that contains sufficient alkali (sodium) to interfere with the growth of most crop plants. (The term is scientifically obsolete, but is still used and understood widely.)

Aquifer: any water-bearing saturated layer of rock, earth or gravel capable of yielding ample supplies of water to bores or springs.

arid climate - Climate in regions that lack sufficient moisture for crop production without irrigation. In cool regions annual precipitation is usually less than 25 cm. It may be as high as 50 cm in tropical regions. Natural vegetation is desert shrubs.

arithmetic mean - A simple average; calculated by summing all item values and dividing by the number of items.

available nutrient - That portion of any element or compound in the soil that can be readily absorbed and assimilated by growing plants ("available" should not be confused with "exchangeable").

balanced design (*statistics*) - An experimental design which has the same number of observations (units) for each level, and where each treatment occurs the same number of times in all levels.

base saturation percentage - The extent to which the adsorption complex of a soil is saturated with exchangeable cations other than hydrogen and aluminum. It is expressed as a percentage of the total cation exchange capacity.

bench terrace (*soil*) - An embankment constructed across sloping fields with a steep drop on the downslope side.

beta level (*statistics*) - Probability of a Type II error, i.e., the probability of accepting the null hypothesis when it is false.

bias (*statistics*) - Systematic error; contrasts with random error.

biennial plant - A plant which completes its life cycle in two years. Plants of this type usually produce leaves and a well-developed root system the first year; stems, flowers, and seeds the second year; and then die.

biomass - The weight of material produced by a living organism or collection of organisms. The term is usually applied to plants to include the entire plant, or it may be qualified to include only certain parts of the plant, e.g., above-ground or leafy biomass. Biomass is expressed in terms of fresh weight or dry weight. In ecological literature, the term biomass refers to the amount of living matter in a given area.

blocking (in experimental design) - A method of gaining precision by reducing the effect of uncontrolled variations on the error of the treatment conditions. Blocking based on a certain variable should decrease variation within a block and increase variation between blocks in order to gain precision.

browse - The buds, shoots, leaves, and flowers of woody plants which are eaten by livestock or wild animals.

budding (*plants*) - The practice of splicing a bud from one tree into the bark of another, usually to obtain high-quality fruit on hardy, established trees.

bulk density, soil - The mass of dry soil per unit of bulk volume, including the air space.

Capillary rise: the upward movement of water caused by molecular attraction between soil particles and water. The action is like water being drawn into a dry sponge. Capillary rise occurs when groundwater is within 1-2 metres of the soil surface.

crop growth rate - The gain in weight of a plant on a unit of area in a unit of time.

cropping pattern - The yearly sequence and spatial arrangement of crops or of crops and fallow on a given area.

cropping system - The cropping patterns used on a farm and their interaction with farm resources, other farm enterprises, and available technology which determine their makeup.

crown - The canopy or top of a single tree or other woody plant that carries its main branches and leaves at the top of a fairly clean stem.

cut-and-carry - Fodder or other plant products which are harvested and carried to a different location to be used or consumed.

cutting (*plant*) - A piece of a branch or root cut from a living plant with the objective of developing roots and growing a new plant, genetically identical to the original parent (a clone).

De-watering bores: these bores were aimed at lowering the watertable in this discharge area to between 3-5 metres below the surface by pumping out some of the groundwater. When groundwater is kept below this level it does not affect the soil surface or underground services such as water pipes.

Discharge area: an area where underground water reaches the soil surface. Loss of vegetation, salt crystals on the soil surface, break up of roads and concrete paths, house brick deterioration, permanent wet areas and rusting underground pipes and metal fences are all signs of a discharge area. To control discharge area watertables, water entering recharge areas must be reduced.

Dryland salinity: Dryland salinity can occur when the amount of water entering the groundwater system is greater than the amount used by plants or drained away.

evaporation - Loss of moisture from surfaces other than plants.

Evaporation basin: these usually large and shallow basins are used to safely dispose of salty groundwater pumped from high watertable areas.

evapotranspiration - The combined loss of water from a given area, and during a specified period of time, by evaporation from the soil surface and by transpiration from plants.

evergreen - Plants which retain their leaves and remain green throughout the year. Opposite of deciduous.

exotic - A plant or animal species which has been introduced outside its natural range. Opposite of indigenous.

experimental treatment - Manipulation of the independent variables of interest, e.g., spacing between plants, fertilizer levels.

experimental unit - The individuals or groups whose behavior is being studied in response to an experimental treatment. The smallest group of subjects that can receive treatment independent of other groups, e.g., a plot.

extensive - Land use or management spread over a large area where land is plentiful (at least for those who control it). Opposite of intensive.

extrapolate - estimating a quantity outside the range of data on which it depends.

Groundwater: the water found in the ground in a saturated zone of soil. Groundwater height varies across the city. It is usually higher in lower parts of the catchment or where there is a change in slope. These areas are often the first sites to be salinity affected.

Piezomete: a non-pumping bore used to measure the level of groundwater below the surface and to allow collection of groundwater for salinity testing. It consists of a sealed PVC pipe 20-40 mm in diameter, with narrow slots cut in the bottom to let ground water enter the pipe. The pipes are usually more than 3 metres deep. The groundwater level readings obtained from piezometers can identify recharge and discharge areas.

Recharge area: where rainfall, irrigation, garden water or water from waterways seep into the ground and add water to the groundwater system.

Rubble pits or sullage pits: these are backyard pits where stormwater collected from house roofs is drained slowly, but directly, into the ground. In recharge and discharge areas these pits can contribute to salinity problems.

Salinisation: is the accumulation of soluble salt within the soil. Soil salt content increases at discharge sites as groundwater evaporates and salts concentrate in the soil. It is harder for plants to remove water from salty soil.

Salinity: a term which refers to salt content in water or soil. It is usually measured in decisiemens per metre (dS/m). The salt concentration of groundwater depends on the salinity content of the soil and rock in which the water is found.

Soil sponge: the drying effect of plant roots drawing water from the soil. Before land clearing, native vegetation provided a soil sponge to a depth of 6 metres or more and a balance existed which prevented excess recharge. In the urban situation not only has our soil sponge been reduced, the amount of water applied has increased as water has been piped from the river.

Urban salinity: salinity occurring in urban areas.

Waterlogging: this occurs when the soil becomes saturated by rising watertables. Plant roots become oxygen starved and sensitive plants eventually die out. Plants more tolerant to saturated conditions such as pinrushes and dock then take over. Underground services are also affected with rusting of water and gas pipes requiring more frequent replacement. Once the watertable reaches the sewer pipe system, salt water can be channelled to the river via the sewerage treatment works.

Watertable: the upper surface of the groundwater. The zone immediately below the watertable is saturated.

Bibliography

Ahern, Col, Shaw, Roger & Thorburn, Peter 1984 'Differences in chemical and physical properties between soil layers of black earths on alluvia in the Lockyer Valley, Queensland', Abstract of conference presentation, in *Proceedings of the National Soils Conference*, Brisbane, May 1984, Australian Society of Soil Science, Brisbane, p. 180.

Asano, T. (1994) Irrigation with treated sewage effluents. Chapter 9, IN *Management of Water Use in Agriculture,* K.K. Tanji and B. Yaron, Editors, Springer Verlag, Berlin, Germany. Ayers, R.S. and Westcot, D.W. (1985) *Water Quality for Agriculture.* FAO Irrigation and Drainage Paper 29 (rev. 1), Rome, Italy.

Christiansen, Ingrid 1993, Distribution and growth of plants in relation to soil salinity in south-east Queensland, BSc (Honours thesis), Department of Botany, University of Queensland, St Lucia.

Davies, C.W. (1962) *Ion Association.* Butterworths Inc., Wash. DC.

Doherty, John 1992, *Some aspects of small-catchment groundwater hydrology*, Project Report QO92001, Department of Primary Industries, Queensland.

Dudley, L.M., and Hanks, R.J. (1991) Model SOWACH: Soil-Plant -Atmosphere -Salinity Management Model (Users Manual). Utah Agri. Exp. Sta. Res. Rept. 140, Logan, Utah.

Food and Agriculture Organization (1989) Production Yearbook, Vol. 42, Rome, Italy.

Gardner, E. (Ted) 1985, 'Hydro-salinity problems in the Lockyer Valley—real and perceived', in *Landscape, soil and water salinity*, Proceedings of the Lockyer– Moreton Regional Workshop, Ipswich, June 1985, Conference and Workshop Series QC85004, pages D1-1 to D1-9, Department of Primary Industries, Queensland.

Ghassemi, F., Jakeman, A.J., and Nix, H.A. (1995) *Salinization of Land and Water Resources*. Univ. of New South Wales Press, Ltd., Canberra, Australia.

Grattan, S.R. (1994) Irrigation with saline waters. Chapter 8, IN *Management of Water Use in Agriculture,* K.K. Tanji and B. Yaron, Editors, Springer Verlag, Berlin, Germany

Halvorson, A.D. (1990) Management of dryland saline seeps. Chapter 17, IN *Agricultural Salinity Assessment and Management* K.K. Tanji, Editor, ASCE Manual No. 71, Amer. Soc. Civil Engrs., New York.

Hoffman, G.J. (1980) Guidelines for the reclamation of salt-affected soils. Pages 49-64, IN Second Inter-Amer. Conf. On Salinity and Water Management Technology, G.A. O'Connor, Editor. Juarez, Mexico.

Hoffman, G.J., Maas, E.V., Prichard, T.L., and Meyer, J.L. (1983) Salt tolerance of corn in the Sacramento-San Joaquin Delta of California, Irrigation Science 4: 31-44.

Hoffman, G.L. (1990) Leaching fraction and roctzone salinity control. Chapter 12, IN *Agricultural Salinity Assessment and Management* K.K. Tanji, Editor, ASCE Manual No. 71, Amer. Soc. Civil Engrs., New York.

Holmes, J.W., and Talsma, T. Editors (1981) *Land and Stream Salinity*. Elsevier Sci. Pub. Co., Amsterdam, The Netherlands.

Hughes, Keith 1982, Summary report on salinity in the Kalbar Area, unpublished internal report, Division of Land Utilisation, Department of Primary Industries, Queensland.

Hughes, Keith 1985, 'Notes on seepage salting at Queensland

Agricultural College Darbalara Farm', in ***Landscape, soil and water salinity***, Proceedings of the Lockyer–Moreton Regional Workshop, Ipswich, June 1985, Conference and Workshop Series QC85004, pp. D2-1 to D2-5, Department of Primary Industries, Queensland.

Hunt, Keryn 1994, 'Boonah: The outfield's fast', Case study in *Saltwatch Activity Book*, Training Series QE94003, Land Conservation, Department of Primary Industries, Queensland, p. 35.

Hutson, J.L., and Wagenet, R.J. (1992) LEACHM: Leaching Estimation and Chemistry Model, version 3, Dept. of Soil, Crop, & Atm Sci. Res. Ser. No. 92-3, Cornell Univ., Ithaca, NY

Jenne, E.A. (1979) *Chemical Modeling in Aqueous Systems.* ACS Symp. Series 93, Amer. Chem. Soc., Wash. D.C.

Karajeh, F.F., and Tanji, K.K. (1994) Agroforestry drainage management model. III. Field salt flow. ASCE *Jour. Irrig. and Drainage Engrg.* 120(2): 397-413.

McNeil, Vivienne, Poplawski, Wojciech & Gardner, E. (Ted) 1991, *Salinity problems affecting irrigation in the Lockyer Valley, Queensland, Australia*, presented at the conference on Irrigated induced physical and chemical changes in groundwater and surface water, Vienna, Austria.

Powell, Bernie, Shaw, Roger & Roberts, Max 1985, 'Factors for evaluation of land for sustainable irrigation in the Lockyer Valley', *in Proceedings Fourth Australian Soil Conservation Conference*, Part 1, ed. I.F. Fergus Maroochydore, Queensland, October 1985, pp. 296–297, Standing Committee on Soil Conservation.

Talbot, R. (Bob), Roberts, Max, McMahon, C. (Ron) & Shaw, Roger 1981, *Irrigation quality of Lockyer Valley alluvia bores during the 1980 drought*, Technical publication No. 5, Department of Biology, Queensland Agricultural College.

Williams, John, Bui, Elizabeth, Gardner, E. (Ted), Littleboy, Mark & Probert, Merv 1997, 'Tree clearing and dryland salinity hazard in the upper Burdekin catchment of north Queensland', *Australian Journal of Soil Research*, 35:785–801.

Index

❑❑❑